BRENT ROBINS

The Perfect Culture

HOPE you
ENJOY IT !

Bret Rob

Cicero Publishing LLC

Contents

Acknowledgement

I would like to thank several people for their tremendous help with this book. My editors provided very valuable feedback: Roisin Heycock, Marcus Banks, Rachel Stout, Christina Hitchcock, and Hannah Jones. Nuno Moreira designed a beautiful cover. Many excellent teachers and professors have taught me so much about how to write well. Finally, I would like to thank my parents; their support in numerous ways helped provide the overseas experiences that are the inspiration for this book.

Visit the author online at www.brentrobinsauthor.com

1

Chapter One

September 2011

"I want everyone at this party drinking, dancing, and having a good time!"

Thomas had started his first year of college at the University of Eastern Indiana just a week ago, and he felt his heartbeat significantly increase as he entered the melee, not sure if he could deliver on the order shouted by the well-built, muscular man standing by the keg. Fortunately, he hadn't had any disputes yet with Sean, his roommate, which had been one of his biggest worries. Thomas was grateful that Sean was unfazed by his trepidation about going to his first college party. Sean had heard about this frat party from someone in his Economics 101 lecture, and since Thomas had no other plans that evening, they went over together. Drinking was officially illegal, but this rule was routinely ignored in the tradition of most college campuses.

Thomas had felt very peaceful in the library earlier in the day, slowly processing his thoughts and letting his mind wander. Here, there were hordes of people. It was very crowded and hard to move around. Instead of trying to push through them all, Thomas made an effort to focus on his surroundings; he'd never been in a real frat house before and he didn't know what to expect. The main room was made of brick. But he couldn't see any brick, as the walls were well masked by the crowd. For Thomas, the ideal physical environment involved a lot of empty space with possibly a small crowd in the room to fill in some of the gaps. This room did not fit the bill; it felt a lot more as if he were incarcerated or being intellectually suffocated.

Thomas was never one to engage in a lot of small talk, and the large amount of background noise further exacerbated this tendency. The frat boys holding court in the center of the room were particularly loud, attempting to prove that they had the most testosterone at the party. Thomas wondered if they were on steroids or were just naturally that obnoxious. *Pass around those steroids that you have*, Thomas thought. *Maybe I wouldn't feel so overwhelmed here if I took whatever you dudes are on at the moment.* He turned to express these thoughts to Sean, but Sean wasn't there. He'd gotten lost in the crowd, possibly, or had gone searching for a drink. Thomas was rooted to the spot, feeling it was safer to stay in one place and let Sean come back to find him rather than venturing further into the pulsing crowd. After about twenty minutes of standing around and listening to the cacophonous shouting of a room full of college kids starting to get intoxicated, Thomas felt that it was probably best to head home. *What am I really going to accomplish here tonight?* he thought, regretting that he had let Sean persuade him to come along. Standing up on his toes, Thomas surveyed the room to find Sean. His roommate was involved in what looked like an intense game of beer pong, fitting in seamlessly with the party. Thomas took a breath and dove into the crowd, elbowing his way towards the drinking game.

"Sean," Thomas said, reaching out to tap his roommate on the shoulder, "I'm going to head back to the dorm. I'm not really enjoying myself here."

"Okay, man. I think you're missing out on a lot of fun, but do as you wish," Sean replied, barely taking his eyes off the cups lined up on the long table.

Once again that week, Thomas mused about how different this reality was from the images that he dreamed of during the summer before starting college. He had imagined sitting around in his dormitory, having fabulous conversations with intellectual soul mates. Is this what college was really about? He had heard that college was "the best four years of your life", but if shouting and getting wasted were going to be the best four years of his life, then what kind of purgatory was he about to enter after he finished college?

He was taking a seminar in Early American History and had high hopes for it since the class was small with only about twenty other students. Therefore, the possibility existed for student participation instead of the professor merely lecturing to a large auditorium, filled with silent students. They'd only had one class so far, but on that first day, the professor caught Thomas's attention with a series of broad questions to the students. "Why do we study history?" was the first. For Thomas, who was deeply studious, this question caused a surge of adrenaline. However, stunned silence came over the rest of the room. He could think of a well-thought-out answer, but before he had a chance to raise his hand, one girl in the front of the room answered, "So that we don't become Communists like the rest of the world." Thomas had to hold back a laugh. To protect us against *Communism?* Communism was almost completely gone. What was this girl taught in high school? Another guy called out that he didn't know or care; he was taking this course as an elective towards his sports management degree. With a large smirk on his face, he added, "I'd rather be playing golf if it were up to me."

Thomas did have some desire to chuckle at the responses. However, it was also quite disheartening that these students had so little knowledge of history or appreciation for it. This was not merely a droll situation; it was also a dark sea. He wondered if the golfer student ever thought about anything more serious than sports. Entering his naturally pensive state of mind, he thought, *Yes, this man exists. He physically exists, and playing golf can be quite enjoyable.* But Thomas thought that there should be something deeper to existence beyond playing a physical sport. *That golfer is an American on his passport. Yet he has no thoughts about what it means to be an American. He didn't have to earn that citizenship. It was automatically given to him merely for being born, and he wastes that opportunity with a superficial, thoughtless existence.*

It then occurred to Thomas that maybe it wasn't so much that the golfer was a person of questionable character. After all, he seemed good-natured enough. Thomas, with his bookishness and penchant for sophisticated humor, was the black sheep in his family of anti-intellectual, heartland folk. However, possibly this golfer would have fit into his family quite well. *Maybe he just has had very limited life experiences, and these experiences have never forced him to consider serious, deeper questions. I would like to get another opinion about this, and I don't know anyone else here yet besides Sean. I am not one to initiate serious conversations with strangers. I will ask Sean what he thinks about this.*

In a very glum state of mind, he remarked, "Sean, I'm the only person in my history seminar who seems to have any appreciation for history."

"Appreciation for history? What does that mean, bro? Did you have a few beers at a party tonight that you haven't mentioned?" Sean replied, laughing heartily.

A look of irritation flashed across Thomas's face. "No, smartass, I didn't have any beers tonight. But I do sometimes wish that nasty-tasting beer would come out of the showers of people who lack appreciation for history. It would serve them right for their blinders. Poetic justice."

Sean looked quite confused by the comment. He paused for a minute, looking like he was trying to figure out what Thomas had meant. Finally, he just shrugged and said, "Okay, dude, I have no idea what you're talking about. Maybe you smoked something tonight much stronger than beer?"

"I have to deny your allegations," Thomas said with a sigh, sitting down on his twin bed covered with the new comforter his mother had bought for him before he left for school. "I do, however, plead guilty to feeling alienated in my history class. I think that history is a fascinating subject, yet one girl in my class thinks that the only reason that we should study history is so that we don't all become Communists. Yes, in the year two thousand fucking eleven, the world is in danger of being overrun by Communism! I've never seen a more astute awareness of the historical context of the early twenty-first century. Another guy who spoke in class today said that he's only taking this class because he needs an elective for his sports management degree, and he would rather be playing golf."

Thomas flopped down on his pillow and closed his eyes, wishing that he'd considered the possibility of attending other schools that were further away from home. He was the first person in his family to go to college. During his final year of high school, the thought of embarking on something so unfamiliar *and* more than an hour from his native surroundings had seemed simply too terrifying. *I could have researched this more thoroughly. As they say, you snooze, you lose.*

"Well guess what, bro, I'd rather be playing golf any day of the week than sitting in a history class. That's why I'm a communications major. That dude and I should have a beer and hang out at the next party. He'd probably stay and have a good time, unlike you who pussied out after thirty minutes." Sean said that last part with more derision than Thomas had been expecting, but at this moment, Thomas was indifferent.

Thomas rose up from the bed and paced back and forth, lightly rolling his eyes. "So elaborate on that point, Sean," he said, ignoring Sean's insult. "Why would you rather play golf than learn about history?"

"Dude, playing golf is fun. History is about as much fun as getting a root canal," Sean replied.

"Do you by chance get hammered before getting a root canal? Where did you go for the last pre-root canal happy hour?"

Now Sean looked even more confused. "I've actually never had a root canal, dude, but it would definitely suck to be sober for it."

"They give you an anesthetic, believe it or not. There are other alternatives besides booze for avoiding a full-blown root canal experience. But anyways, back to my original question. Why do you think that history is painfully boring?" Thomas asked.

"Because who cares what happened in the past? I want to have fun right now, and playing golf sounds like a ton of fun on a nice day, bro," Sean said.

"Would you say the same thing about your own life? Everything that happened in your own life up until today: does it have any meaning or importance?"

"Sure, but what does this have to do with history?" Sean asked.

"Your life is history at the micro level. If history at the micro level is important, then it seems reasonable to believe that history at the macro level would be important as well," Thomas said, looking away at the wall. He attempted to remain unruffled, even though it was demoralizing to hear more anti-history viewpoints at his university.

Sean shook his head a full three times before speaking. "I'm getting pretty exhausted from this conversation, Thomas. I'm here at college to have a good time and get my degree so that I can get a job when I finish and pay my own bills. You seem harmless enough, but if you want to sit around having these pointless conversations, then you need to find a different crowd. Cool?"

"Well, Sean, I hope that someday you change your mind. It isn't going to happen tonight though; I can see that."

Thomas really wished that Sean was an anomaly at his school, but he wasn't. Thomas himself was the anomaly. He was one of the only people on campus who saw the value of learning as an end in itself. For just about everyone else, they saw their college classes in the exact same light as Sean: simply a ticket to a job, and nothing more.

His experience in high school had been quite similar. Almost no other classmates enjoyed having the kind of probing conversations that fascinated him. They usually reacted in a similar manner as Sean had. Thomas had been hoping that college, that supposed ideal four years of life, was going to be different. Here he would find others to explore ideas with. Intellectual conversations would be robust dialogues with other people, not merely him talking to a nicely painted wall. Instead, it looked like his college years were just going to be the next exit on the same boring highway.

September 2014.

Three years later, Thomas was now a senior at the University of Eastern Indiana. He no longer had a roommate to argue with; seniors were able to get single rooms quite easily. Most of his fellow seniors had moved into apartments where they could drink and party more easily and avoid the Communists who might try and knock on their doors and convert them.

Most of his classmates were starting to talk about looking for jobs, or at least general career planning. It was easiest to look for a job in the surrounding area. Certainly that was one option, but he was yearning for a change. His college experience had mirrored his high school experience: lonely, isolated, and alienated. In this part of the United States that he had experienced, he was a square peg in a round hole. His family had never left the state due to lack of interest and tight budgets. He didn't know if the rest of America was different from where he had grown up. Although his college classes had not helped in this regard, they had, nonetheless, expanded his worldview.

That day, while studying in the library, he pondered serious thoughts about expanding his horizons and traveling overseas after graduation. On the bright side, his college classes had given him a greater *theoretical* awareness about lands beyond American borders, but Thomas strongly preferred to have real, tactile experiences of these places. Showing would be far more meaningful than telling. He knew that France historically had a café culture where people actually did sit in cafés and have the types of discussions that Thomas liked. He also knew that India was a deeply spiritual place; it sounded like a society where getting the next big car or large television wasn't everyone's first priority. He still remembered his professor lecturing about

8

people bathing in the holy Ganges River; this gave him a lot of food for thought. Sure, many of his classmates were hypocritical Christians who prayed at church and then drank heavily and cheated on their significant others. But the Hindus who bathed in that Ganges River sounded more sincere to him. Possibly they truly believed in the teachings of their religion? Possibly they took spirituality and the soul as serious ideas to heart? He wanted to talk to these people who bathed in the Ganges. He thought that he would probably learn more from talking to these people than his college classmates, and they would definitely be more rewarding company.

None of this was absolutely certain. However, Thomas did know for sure that he was unhappy in rural Indiana. He was hoping that there was a paradise somewhere on earth. Was France his paradise? What about Japan, where a lot of his electronics came from? He had learned that Japan was full of Shinto shrines. Surely there was somewhere where he would not feel alienated and life might approach bliss? He didn't know exactly where this place was, but French cafés, Indian spirituality, and Japanese shrines all sounded immensely appealing, and extremely far away from Indiana.

I am not staying here for the rest of my life. He could do that, and have a modern-day version of Dante's Inferno. Or he could find a different experience that would open up his mind to different ideas, different cultures, and at a minimum, different surroundings. Just because college had been a major disappointment did not justify feeling completely forlorn about the future. *Many famous people have recovered from setbacks,* Thomas thought. He remembered that Einstein had difficulty obtaining a teaching post before he went to graduate school. *I may not be Einstein. I may not even be as talented as the founders of*

Einstein Brothers' Bagels. Doc Brown's dog Einstein in <u>Back to the Future</u> *had resolve though, and so will I.*

The next day, after class, Thomas went over to the Office of International Programs, headed by Dr. Dick Cheesemeister. *Interesting last name*, Thomas thought. *He may wind up steering me towards France with that name.* The office was filled with books about different countries from all over the world; some of them he had never heard of before, such as Burma and Kazakhstan. He saw materials about work opportunities abroad in Suriname. *Yes, people in Eastern Indiana must be lining up to go to Suriname,* Thomas thought with a smirk. *Hell, I've never heard of it and I'm probably one of the few people on this campus who has even visited this office. Maybe if they bribe some of my classmates with a few kegs of beer and some porn magazines, they'd think about working there for a while.*

After a few minutes, a tall blonde girl came up to him and asked him if he needed any help. Thomas was startled. He'd been so immersed in the books on the shelf that he hadn't heard her enter.

"Yes, I want to work abroad after I graduate. I need to experience something else besides rural Indiana," he said, turning to face her.

The girl smiled, just barely. "What is your major here?"

"History, with a minor in straightforward irony," he said.

She did not find his wry humor endearing. Instead, her vibe reminded him of Mr. Keating in *Dead Poets Society* slamming his hand on the bell and replying, "Thank you for playing." She gave a little annoyed huff before answering, "Well, there might not be a lot of programs where you can directly use your major. Are you just looking for any kind of work experience?"

"Yes, I think that will serve my purposes. Where is the

information on France?"

"The European programs are around the back wall by that green plant. We have a lot of programs in Europe. I am confident that you will find something to your liking," she said flatly.

Thomas thanked the girl, who had already disappeared again, for her help and headed over to the European section. In one binder, he saw a decent-sized listing of programs in France. One of them involved child-care work. He wasn't going to do that. He found the noisy, rowdy behavior of young children very annoying. Another one was to be an agricultural volunteer working for a small stipend; that didn't appeal to him either. He thought it would be too exhausting working on a farm, and he didn't want to be in yet another rustic setting. He preferred more of a contrast to his environment in Indiana, so an urban experience would be more suitable. Then he came across one program that permitted foreigners to work in French hotels for a few months. Temporary visas were available, and the program was operating in several French cities. He felt a small spark light up inside. *I will get to experience urban life and I think that I can tolerate hotel work for a few months.* He copied down the important contact information and walked back to his room, in high spirits and much more optimistic than he had been during the last few years. That evening, he filled out the paperwork to obtain a passport and completed the application to the program.

2

Chapter Two

June 2015

"Passengers, please note that the fasten seatbelt light has been turned off. You are now free to move about the cabin. Our estimated arrival in Paris is 4:00 p.m. local time."

This was Thomas's first time leaving the country, and the second time that he'd ever even been on a plane. His stomach was in knots, and he was unable to keep his toes still. It was one thing to be excited about the *opportunity* to work in France; actually acting on this feeling was a totally different matter altogether. One only had to ask Hamlet about the thought–action conundrum, if it were possible to speak to fictional characters. Thomas's French was very limited; he'd taken a four-month course in preparation for the trip, but that had barely taught him more than how to ask for the bathroom and to conjugate the verb être. Furthermore, he didn't know anyone there. But he had to go on this adventure. The alternative was staying in Indiana, a place where he felt such deep alienation and boredom that he thought that he would lose his mind. When the stewardess came around,

Thomas asked for a nice glass of Merlot wine, which helped calm the anxiety somewhat. *Look at me! I'm already enjoying a pleasing glass of wine and I haven't even arrived there yet.*

His only previous time on a plane had been a very short domestic flight. It was not customary for Thomas to be in such a confined space for an extended period of time. After several hours in the air, he strongly wished that he could unwind on a cozy bed in a hotel room. *Claustrophobia is a genuine concern. It's as if I'm in a picture, but the photographer keeps cropping my dimensions. Pretty soon, I'll be a mere afterthought in the photo.* Returning to concrete reality, he noted: *Next time, I am definitely booking an aisle seat. It is indeed enjoyable to be able to see the scenery from the window, but I am feeling too constricted. Every time that I need to go to the bathroom, both of the other people have to get up as well.*

Several hours later, Thomas woke up to the sound of the plane hitting the ground. He had arrived at Charles de Gaulle International Airport in Paris. The beginning of "Bohemian Rhapsody" perfectly captured the moment: "Is this the real life, Is this just fantasy?" He stood up and reached for his bag, trembling as he walked off the plane. How would he be able to communicate his needs before he began his language immersion classes? Would anyone speak English?

One of the flight attendants said, "Bonne journée, Monsieur," as Thomas exited. He did know that Monsieur was roughly translated as "sir" in English. *Wow, I get called "sir" here without ever having worn a military uniform or firing a weapon. Not a bad arrangement.*

As he entered the airport, he saw that the signs were mostly both in English and French. He breathed a sigh of relief. At least he wouldn't get lost in the airport. *Tom Hanks was paid to sleep in*

*an airport for months. I will not receive any such compensation. It is
critical that I can make it out of here.* That would be French task
number one.

First, he had to pass through the immigration line. For the
first time in his existence, Thomas was required to stand in a line
marked for "foreigners". *I really am in a foreign land now.*

"Parlez-vous français?" the man asked.

"No, sir."

"Okay. What is the purpose of your visit to France?" *He does
speak some English. Thank goodness!*

"I am participating in a program for foreigners, in which we
work in hotels on a tourist visa." *I am nervous about giving him
the "wrong" answer. What if he does not like my response?*

"And where you will be working and staying?"

"I will be working at a hotel in Bordeaux and I will be staying
with a host family. Here is the address of their home." He handed
the address to the man. *I am really exhausted from this long flight.
Interview, please end soon! The man seems a bit brusque, but I was
expecting this, based on common French stereotypes.*

"How long will you stay in France?"

"Three months."

"When do you leave for Bordeaux?"

"Today."

"I would like to see your ticket and boarding pass."

Thomas handed over these documents.

"Good. Bonne chance, Monsieur."

"Thank you," Thomas replied. Although Thomas loved to be
sarcastic and biting with others, he figured that this was probably
not the ideal situation to break out his wit. Too many wisecracks
would probably just make the immigration official suspicious.

After passing the immigration test, Thomas boarded his connecting flight to Bordeaux. The domestic flight had a French lunch of a cucumber salad with vinaigrette dressing, chicken skewer with ratatouille, brie cheese, and a kiwi for dessert. *This is damn good. Now I understand why they have a big ego about their food; it's merely an airplane meal!*

He exited the plane to more French greetings from the staff and made his way through the much smaller airport, scanning the crowd in the arrivals hall until he saw a sign that said "Thomas Gephardt". He looked to the middle-aged couple holding the sign who were flanked by two young girls. That must be the Roux family he was expecting to see. The father was well dressed with dress pants and a well-pressed green shirt. He was quite fit, much more fit than most of the people in his hometown in Indiana. *He's clearly not eating enough McDonald's*, Thomas thought. *I'll try to convince him of the merits of being fat and out of shape.* The mother wore a nice-looking dress and she was fit as well. They both had pretty stoic expressions. Thomas took a deep breath and approached them.

"Good afternoon, Mr. Gephardt," the man said with a heavy French accent. "I am Paul Roux. This is my wife, Marie, and my two daughters, Noelle and Colette. We will be your hosting family here in Bordeaux. Please come this way," he added with a very slight smile. Thomas shook his hand and forced a smile of his own at Noelle and Colette. *Maybe these children will be better behaved. Even if they are not, at least I can learn some French from them. Yes, a French brat is preferable to an Indiana one.* They made their way to a very compact car, which was much smaller than the gas guzzlers that Thomas was used to seeing cruise around the streets of Indiana. The youngest girl, Noelle, sat on the mother's lap in order for all of them to fit. As modest as the car may have been, this did not seem to prevent Paul in any way from driving as if he were driving an expensive race car. *Getting into an accident because of this madman is not a great way to start my French journey,* Thomas thought, gripping the side of his seat. Although Thomas was an atheist, he was starting to wish that he had some kind of God to pray to. Marie and the girls seemed to be completely unfazed by Paul's driving. Marie sat in the front seat with the same consistently expressionless look on her face, mostly just making sure that Noelle didn't fly through the windows every few minutes from Paul's sharp turns.

Miraculously, Thomas and everyone else made it to their modest condo. His smart-aleck brain was still in one piece. Thomas supposed everyone else was used to Paul's erratic driving from years of these rides. He considered that it is human nature to become accustomed to many things from enough exposure, just as it had been second nature for so many of his college classmates to be apathetic about learning and enthusiastic about drinking enormous amounts of alcohol. *In that respect, these French people are not radically different from my classmates back home. They are creatures of habit, and they adapt to the conditions that are around them.*

Once they were inside the condo, Paul showed Thomas his room. He quickly scanned it. The Roux family would all fit in here, barely. It was about the same size as his dormitory room in college, albeit without the boisterous partiers always shouting outside. It was nicely decorated with art and it had a nice-looking desk with a computer. There was no television in the room, though Thomas had noticed one in the main room.

"Is the TV in the family room the only one in the house?" he asked.

"Yes, we do not take lots of hours watching television. Marie and I try to encourage our daughters to spend more time in books than in front of a television."

Hmm...this is a family that emphasizes reading. This was quite a contrast to his mother and father's household where the television was constantly blaring. His mother loved sitcoms and soap operas and watched a minimum of five hours of television per day.

"Do you like books, Thomas?" Paul asked, with a skeptical look.

"Yes, I do. I think that a quieter, book-oriented household will be a nice thing, Paul."

"Good," Paul said, again with his slight smile. *He seems to be a bit surprised by my answer.*

I don't think that Paul is ever going to make it as a Walmart greeter with his weak smiles. Then again, if Thomas had been really psyched about becoming a Walmart greeter, he never would have needed to embark on a plane to France. Did those big smiles at Walmart really mean anything anyway? The greeters were smiling because they were required to by their employer and supervisors. It wasn't the kind of spontaneous, romantic smile that might have some deeper meaning. It was more similar to picking up a fork and knife or turning on a light switch; it was merely done out of habit and as a requirement. So to be bothered by Paul's fainter smiles did not make logical sense to Thomas. He was probably just a genuine person who didn't see the point of big smiles for no reason.

Thomas slept in a peaceful state of mind for several hours that evening, but woke up at four in the morning due to jet lag. *If this had happened to me all the time during college, I could have studied a lot before class*, he thought, groggily checking the clock. Eventually he fell back asleep and woke up again at 10:00 a.m. *I lost the race to be the first person to smile faintly today in this household. Paul is probably already ahead by one hundred on that count.*

When he ventured out of his room, Marie turned towards him. "Good morning, Thomas. I put some new towels in zee bathroom for your douche—I mean, shower."

"Thanks, Marie." *Great, they already think that I'm a douchebag for sleeping in late*, Thomas thought, berating himself. Then he realized that it might just be a French term and he didn't need to take any offense. He made a mental note to check his French dictionary later.

"Tonight, we will take you out for a nice French dinner. Get some rest today; you have had a long trip."

In the evening, the family and Thomas walked over to a lavishly decorated French restaurant a couple of streets over from the Rouxs' building. The walls were well covered with paintings by famous French artists such as Monet and Renoir, including portraits of Cardinal Richelieu and Louis XIV. Thomas was stunned to be eating in the presence of the Sun King. *I do not want to disappoint him by being a boorish American and guzzling down my beer and belching extremely loudly*, he thought, not that Thomas had ever guzzled beer and rarely belched loudly.

The waiter spoke only French, so Paul and Marie translated. "We will translate for you tonight, but I hope to see you speak some French as your stay increases," Paul said with a wink. The wink felt slightly warmer than his faint smiles.

"Sounds reasonable," Thomas replied.

"Thomas, what would you like to drink? The wine menu is on the third page."

"I will just have an apple juice," he replied, not bothering to peruse the wine list.

A look of deep shock spread over the faces of all four members of the family. "You usually drink apple juice for the dinner?" Marie asked.

"I do sometimes. It seems strange to you?"

"Oui, uh, yes, I have never had this drink for zee dinner," Marie said. "But order what you like." They translated for the waiter, who then also looked at Thomas as if he would be bringing a drink to an alien from outer space. Marie and Paul both ordered glasses of red wine.

"I said to the waiter that you are American," Paul said.

Well, that should resolve everything! Now the waiter knows that I'm an uncivilized fool who doesn't know how to order a drink properly at a nice French dinner. Thomas was used to viewing his classmates as unsophisticated. It felt quite strange to have the tables turned.

"People who drink apple juice have a tendency to drive very carefully," Thomas remarked.

Paul and Marie looked quite puzzled after hearing this. For a moment, Thomas could imagine them exhaling cigarette smoke, in the shape of question marks.

"Where did you hear this information?" Paul asked.

"Well, we have an expression in English that an apple a day keeps the doctor away. It is a logical conclusion from that."

Paul and Marie did not pick up any hint that Thomas was attempting to be humorous, or that he was indirectly referring to Paul's maniac driving style.

"Apple juice is not apple, Thomas. It is mostly sugar," Marie said. "Do they not teach you this in America?"

"I'm sorry, Marie. I was trying to be a little bit funny, but humor sometimes gets lost in translation and cultural experiences."

Marie lightly nodded her head, unsmiling as usual.

"As you become more familiar with zee French language, I hope that you can make us laugh more. It will take time to understand," Paul reassured him.

"It will give me a goal to work on. I'll start eating apples instead of ordering apple juice at fancy French restaurants. Hopefully that will at least help begin the process," Thomas said, smiling broadly, hoping that they could be done with this portion of the conversation.

No such luck. Their expressions continued to remain stoic and the children were starting to look pretty bored. A few minutes later, the waiter returned with a bottle of apple juice and two large glasses of wine.

"You have decided what to order for the meal?" Paul asked.

"Do you have any recommendations for my first meal here?"

"I would suggest the coq au vin. It is a very traditional French dish that is chicken marinated in red wine."

"Can I order it marinated in apple juice instead?" *I am still unable to shake off my sardonic thoughts.*

"No."

"Okay. I will have the coq au vin," Thomas replied, badly mangling the correct French pronunciation. *Maybe I am committing an error making jokes about the food this early in our relationship. Or to be more culturally relevant, I am probably committing a faux pas.*

Paul ordered a rabbit stew and Marie ordered a braised duck. The waiter also brought some fresh-looking baguettes to the table.

Paul spoke to his daughters in French for several minutes while Thomas was enjoying the bread. He was completely clueless about what was being said. *This is kind of nice being able to zone out of conversations due to language. Back in Indiana, I always know the idiotic things that everyone is saying. Zoning out of a lot of the college conversations would have been quite pleasurable.*

He thought again of the beginning of "Bohemian Rhapsody". *This is not fantasy. Surely, Descartes was correct. I think, therefore I am. This meal is real, and it is so flavorsome.* Thomas couldn't remember ever having such a fine, exquisite meal in a restaurant; the dining options in his hometown were quite limited. The coq au vin was richly seasoned and tender. The apple juice didn't seem to go all that well with the rest of the meal, so Thomas did understand the initial sneers from his host family and the waiter a bit more.

This will probably happen to me quite a bit during this overseas experience. I will say something or commit an act that others find strange or odd. Part of traveling is that I just need to take these experiences in good stride and learn from them. If overseas travel were really angst free all the time without any challenges, then I wouldn't grow as much from the experience. This life is like a very bumpy road with many trips, falls, and bleeding skin before progressing to the destination. This thought somewhat reassured him.

As they finished up the main course, Marie suggested to Thomas that he order a dessert. "It is good to try French desserts, Thomas. We enjoy our sweets here and you should share zee experience."

"Yes, I agree," he said. "Let's see a dessert menu."

Thomas noticed that they had to call the waiter over whenever they needed to speak to him. In the U.S., he was used to the waiter frequently coming over, asking how things were going and asking if they needed anything else, with a large smile and bubbly enthusiasm. This waiter did not smile and put on no air of strong enthusiasm. He was very to the point. Maybe since the tip is already included, he doesn't feel this pressure to be a salesman as much. The service did not seem to be as good, but it was refreshing to get a bit more personal space from the waiter and he didn't feel pressured at all to leave to make space for new diners. He thought that people who value attentiveness and interaction would prefer the American style. People who want to just be left alone and only interact when needed would definitely prefer it the French way.

Soon, the waiter brought the dessert menu. "What would you recommend that I order?" Thomas asked Marie.

"For your first time ordering a French dessert, I think that a crepe is a good idea. We are very famous for the crepes," she said with immense pride.

Following her advice, he ordered a crepe with chocolate sauce and vanilla ice cream. Marie and her husband ordered a raspberry brûlée. The older daughter ordered a chocolate mousse. *Hmm, I never associated a chocolate mousse with France before. It certainly does sound French though, when I think about it.* The dessert was a true feast for the eyes, nose, and mouth. Like the main course, it was fit for a king, including Louis XIV himself. *Almost everyone that I've seen here is pretty thin. How can this be, eating all of this buttery food and with all of these mouth-watering sweet desserts?* He did recall hearing something about the "French paradox" at some point when he was growing up, but he didn't know exactly what that was. He had noticed, however, that the portion sizes were significantly smaller in this restaurant compared to most of his dining experiences at home. The amount of chicken in his main dish had been fairly small, and the crepe was not particularly large either. *I should ask them about this.*

"Paul, how do the French stay healthy? My travel book said that the food has a lot of butter, and Marie said that you enjoy sweets as well."

"We drink much wine, which is good for the heart. We do not eat much between meals and the amount of food that we eat is not so much," he replied.

"So I can eat as much butter as I want as long as I wash it down with a glass of wine?" Thomas asked.

"This is taking my argument to extreme logic. But I believe that it is reasonable to say that our wine drinking helps wash out bad effects from a lot of butter consumption," Paul replied.

He sensed the beginnings of another stimulating intellectual conversation. This was right up his alley. Thomas had loved learning from a young age, despite his family's provincial leanings. It was a bit of a mystery where this intellectual curiosity had come from. Possibly it was a "genetic mutation" in his family?

Paul's remarks sounded reasonable to Thomas, and he nodded in assent. This seemed to be a gray area of health science. It wasn't all black and white. It appeared that it was still possible to have good health indicators despite consuming a lot of unhealthy foods. It was also interesting that alcohol, which was something that was condemned by many as being unhealthy, could be healthy in certain circumstances. Clearly guzzling six cans of beer in one night was not healthy. He had always associated only negative images with alcohol because of his college experiences. But drinking a nice glass of wine at a fancy restaurant could be healthy since it was with a meal and it was a moderate amount.

The meal had been his first "real" experience of French culture. Sitting in Paul's "race car" had been experiencing the culture to some extent, but it was relatively brief and did not compare to the fullness of feasting on an exquisite French meal with several courses. Getting to this point had not been a bed of roses. He had wondered several times if he had made the right decision taking the plunge into this experience. But now the regret had completely dissipated. He could do this. He *should* do this.

For Thomas, this meal truly was second to none. No meal back home had been comparable. That was in large part a reflection of growing up in a small town with limited dining options and having parents who did not travel nor try to expose him to different experiences. He did not harbor strong antipathy towards his parents, feeling that they were creatures of habit like everyone else. He was more focused on his gratitude for having the opportunity to expand beyond his family confines. He thought that it must indeed be possible to have a great meal in larger cities in the United States. He had heard of some New York City fans calling it the "capital of the world". *Would they say something like this if it were impossible to have great food in the city? Surely not!* But the fact that he had experienced it in a foreign country added something to the experience. He had fumbled his way through ordering a drink, shocking the rest of his party. However, the experience of the main course and dessert overshadowed that. The coq au vin had a rich, buttery flavor. The zucchini was elegantly seasoned with clove, thyme, basil, and garlic. Finally, the icing on the cake was the freshly baked crepe, free of preservatives and other chemicals. *Just two bites of the crepe were worth the cost of the plane ticket alone.*

Thomas was a big fan of the U2 song "Sleep like a Baby Tonight". He did indeed sleep like a baby that evening, still jet-lagged. When he woke up the next morning and entered the dining area, Paul informed Thomas that he was going to take him to the language school today to register for classes. "You will also learn about culture when you take your classes. You will learn that we like wine with our meals," Paul said, winking very slightly.

Everything is very slight with this guy, Thomas thought. Slight smiles. Slight winks. King of subtlety. *Maybe that's why some of the French movies that I have seen don't have such a clear plot compared to mainstream Hollywood films. Maybe this is a more subtle culture.* The beaming Walmart greeters with the huge plastic smiles and the smiling cashiers belting out "have a great day!" just would not fit the scene here. *It is a land of opaque, convoluted artistry,* Thomas believed. *It may take a lot of patience to understand a lot of the subtleties and nuances. Everything will not be easily comprehensible from day one here. This may truly be like the real-life version of a French film where the plot is not easily defined, and at times, I get very frustrated from the lack of clear meaning and direction. But some of these vague French films have been ultimately satisfying when I persevered through them. Hopefully this experience will also be that way.*

Later that day, in the afternoon, they walked to the language school to register for French classes. The weather was quite sunny and picturesque. Thomas was used to mostly gray days in the gritty Midwest. It was quite rare to experience a day that was filled with this much sunshine. He had not previously associated France with the sun, but it was his understanding that certain regions did receive copious amounts of it.

"Does Paris have a lot of sunny days?" he asked.

Mentioning Paris seemed to cause a not so subtle frown on Paul's face. "In Bordeaux, we prefer to think that this is a much nicer place to live. More sincere people and a more relaxed pace of life. And yes, we have much more sun than the Parisians," he said with a half-smile. It was the biggest smile that Thomas had ever seen come out of him! *So that is how I get more passion out of Paul! He expresses his passion either by almost breaking the gas pedal in the car from excessive force or by denouncing Paris. I better not declare any strong allegiances to the capital while I am living in his home. I do not want to wake up inside a guillotine, finding that my shirt is soaked in blood and apple juice.*

He had never considered before that there would be regional rivalries or inter-city rivalries in France. It was not surprising though. Certainly these kinds of feelings existed in the U.S., so it made sense that regionalism also existed in other places. There is a tendency to view the citizens in other places just primarily as foreigners; they clearly are not part of your country, so they are foreign. But beneath that foreign identity are also numerous other sub-identities, and one of these sub-identities is based on regions. *What a complicated world this is. Just staying in rural Indiana has shielded me from a gigantic amount of global complexity. I have now entered the global pool for the first time, but I am still in the very shallow waters. It's only my first foreign experience, and it has been a mere few days since I arrived.*

As they continued walking through town, Thomas saw a prominent arch. He had certainly never seen anything of the sort back home, where the biggest attraction was the state fair that set up camp once a year. He asked Paul, "What is that?"

"That is the Victory Arch from the Roman period," Paul replied nonchalantly, as if it were nothing for him to see ancient Roman architecture in his city. For Thomas though, this was incredible. Something that had survived since the days of the Romans! *Clearly these people have been here a long time to perfect baking their baguettes and snorting their cheeses.* He understood a bit more why he had heard that a lot of French people looked down their noses at Americans (even if cheese sometimes fell out), viewing them as naïve and ignorant. America, compared to any of the European countries, *was* a youthful nation. That perception squared with a lot of his college experience, and the appreciation for history was certainly far less pronounced in his home area. Thomas remembered how history had meant nothing to most of the students in his history classes. Paul wasn't awestruck by the Roman arch because he was used to it. Despite its ubiquity, he could tell just from talking to Paul that he did strongly value the importance of history. Paul had previously said to him that it was not possible to understand the society and culture that you come from without a thorough knowledge of its history. He had said something along the lines of: "If you do not know any of your history, you are walking blind, even with your eyes fully open." Thomas could not agree more.

The historical experience on this walk did not end there. They also passed by Bordeaux Cathedral, which was mostly built in the fourteenth and fifteenth centuries. However, its history dated back to the 1100's, including the wedding of Louis XII and Eleanor of Aquitaine. Thomas knew about Notre Dame Cathedral from his history classes, but he refrained from making a comparison to Paris. *I may not make it back home tonight if I mention Paris again. I need to put Paris out of my mind. It is the capital, but there is clearly a lot more to France than just Paris. My experience is going to be mostly here in Bordeaux, and to quote Mr. Keating from* Dead Poets Society, *I need to suck all the marrow out of this local experience. I will make Bordeaux into a thrilling experience, and follow Billy Crystal's advice: "Forget Paris!"*

They were at the language school. The building was impressive. It was a fairly old, quaint stone structure. It had majestic door handles that evoked an older, regal era. "Is this a well-known language school?" he asked Paul.

"I have dined with one of the owners a few times. He also is involved in Bordeaux wines and he will give you a better price for your study," Paul replied.

That should be a great way to learn French if we get served good wine all the time and I'm always too wasted to remember anything that I am learning. I will come back home and people will ask me about my French language experience, and I will tell them that I didn't learn a word of French, but I got to sample all of the best wines in Bordeaux! Which will be a more meaningful cultural experience: learning French while actually in France, or being exposed to numerous different delicious wines? Of course, if my main goal is just to drink good wine, I could have done that back home. French wine is probably available in Indiana somewhere, not that I ever went out searching for it.

Because of Paul's personal connection, Thomas was able to sign up for French lessons at a slightly below market rate. He would have lessons four days a week, which would accommodate his work schedule. He would find out his work schedule at the hotel in a couple of days, and he hoped to learn at least some rudimentary French before then. The language school offered classes at enough different times that he would not have a problem finding lessons around his work schedule, he was assured.

"You will have the first lesson today. Do you remember how to walk home from here, or should I come back here after your lesson concludes?" Paul asked.

Thomas knew that he would definitely not be able to walk back to his host family's home without becoming extremely lost. The streets were not familiar to him at all with foreign-sounding names and they were also very curved and angular, so it was much more difficult to navigate around. *This deep history does have that as a consequence*, Thomas realized. Indiana is so comparatively young that they built the roads to be very straight. The second reason that he knew that walking back alone successfully was a quite forlorn possibility was that his mind had been aimlessly

28

wandering the whole time with thoughts about *Dead Poets Society*, sucking all the marrow out of life, Billy Crystal, and numerous other distractions.

Paul does not realize this. He thinks that I was just completely focused on the sensory sights around us. He has no idea how far off my mind wandered on this journey. There is something thrilling in that sense about mental journeys. Our mental journeys are largely hidden from others, unless we choose to make statements about them through spoken language. Otherwise, if we do not do that, the mind is hidden ether. We are free to travel down any road that we please in our mind, or any bridge, any ocean.

"I will meet you after class here. Thanks, Paul."

Thomas was then escorted into a small classroom where three other students were already waiting. "Welcome to Rue du Tournesol language school. My name is Pierre and I will be your teacher for your lessons. Today we will use much English since you do not speak French. As time continues, I hope that more of our classes will be in French," he said with a smile that was one-sixteenth slighter than Paul's. *They really hone them on this slight smile thing. I need to get Pierre and Paul at a table for a contest to see who can still smile, but in the slightest way possible.*

"Now we will learn a little bit about each person before we begin our study of French."

Thomas learned that he was studying with Canadian John, German Angela, and Japanese Jinsei. John said that he had learned French in school since it was Canada's other language, but he had not been a good student. He was hoping to give French a second chance. Angela said that she wanted to understand her European neighbor better by learning the language and hopefully picking up some knowledge about the culture. "We have had a lot of conflicts in our history and I want to try to understand the people here," she said.

Again, someone was talking about the importance of history. Thomas was surprised to be hearing this so much. In some respects, he was beginning to feel like much less of an outsider in Bordeaux than in Indiana. True, he did not speak the language here and was unfamiliar with many of the customs, such as what to order for drinks with his meals. But for the first time, he did not feel strange about having an interest in history. When Thomas had first arrived in France, he kept thinking about the beginning of "Bohemian Rhapsody". But at least with regard to his liking for history, he was far less bohemian here compared to his birthplace. *It doesn't have to be that I feel like a complete outsider for being intellectual. Here, the "normal" people grasp the importance of history. What is normal anyway? How can it be "normal" in rural Indiana to be completely ignorant of history and "normal" here to be deeply enthralled by history?* He knew from his history classes that cultural norms within the same place changed over time anyway. It was also obvious that cultural norms were relative to both time and the physical place, or space. *It would have been easier to survive my college days if I had known that there was a place like this. I do not think that I would have become as upset about my alienation. The alienation was so painful because I thought sometimes that the whole world was similar to my university, and I was destined to be the odd man out anywhere. This time here is a lifesaver just for this realization alone.*

Angela did not smile at all; she looked stone-faced serious. She did not laugh at any of his attempts to be sarcastic. When Thomas introduced himself, he said that he partly wanted to come to France to eat better quality fast food. John laughed immediately, but Angela merely shrugged her shoulders in confusion. Jinsei also had a blank expression when he said this. However, Jinsei's

English was somewhat limited, so Thomas thought that possibly he did not understand the humor due to language issues. Angela, however, spoke English quite well, so he was not sure why she did not see any humor in his comment. Apparently merely liking history did not mean that she would necessarily be an enjoyable classmate.

I do not want to make too many generalizations about a culture from one example. I will be able to generalize about the French because I will be meeting many of them during this period. But to start forming conclusions about Germans based on one classmate? That sounds too premature. However, the fact that she shared with Paul and others here a strong interest in history suggested to Thomas that it was highly likely that this was a common European characteristic. Clearly, each European country had its own distinct culture and language, but because of a shared history and interactions between the different countries, they also probably shared common characteristics as well. It was not surprising that people who had grown up in older countries would have a stronger appreciation for history. For them, history was not just an abstract concept in a book, as it was in Indiana. They saw it in their streets, castles, and former royal palaces. History was tangible here.

When Jinsei introduced himself, he seemed to shake at each word of English that he used. He first said, "My English not good," and then lightly laughed. He said that he liked traveling, and he wanted to see how Europeans lived. He was quite stylishly dressed, with funky jeans and an expensive watch. He had been playing games on a mini electronic device when Thomas had first entered the classroom.

Some of his college classmates had told him that they thought that it would be "too scary" to go to Europe. They were shocked that he had the "courage" to jump on a plane and visit a different country. *Well, if I had enough courage to leave my hometown and study at a university, is it that big of a leap to travel to another country?*

Some of these same classmates who were absolutely horrified at the thought of going to another country were fearless at parties and bars when it came to approaching women. Thomas found approaching women whom he did not know much more intimidating than merely hopping on a plane and experiencing Bordeaux. *What causes fear is subjective*, he thought. *There are no universal rules. An exhilarating feeling for one person is a traumatic experience for another.*

The first French lesson was fairly intense. They learned how to pronounce various sounds in the French alphabet, numerous common words such as bonjour, au revoir, and merci. They also learned a few fundamental verbs and how to conjugate them. Thomas could clearly see that French was not an easy language to pronounce. There was no means of knowing how to pronounce "au revoir" merely by looking at it; it was necessary to hear it from a French speaker and to force the mouth into unnatural shapes for an English speaker. There were many silent letters as well.

From the first day's lesson, he understood more now why Paul's accent had its distinctiveness. His speech patterns had been formed by speaking his native tongue and therefore, when he spoke a foreign language, those effects were apparent. That was why Jinsei and Angela also had their own distinct accents. He now was cognizant of the fact that he should have more respect for people who speak English as a foreign language. *This is no easy task to pronounce all of these foreign sounds, remember all of these unfamiliar words, and conjugate all of the verbs correctly! Just putting together one completely correct sentence is no small feat!* Language was a lot like culture in this respect. Just as I am very comfortable with certain foods and certain clothing styles, I am also very comfortable with certain sounds in my language. It was easily observable that Jinsei had difficulty pronouncing the letter "L" when he spoke English. When he said the word "English", it sounded as though he was saying "Engrish". Thomas had much greater sympathy for Jinsei's struggle now; he had equal difficulty pronouncing many French words. But Thomas felt that even if he learned to speak French fluently, he would still never feel that he was "one of them" in this land. *After twenty-two years of living in Indiana, could I ever really be one of them? Even if I become completely comfortable conversing in their language, will I ever feel totally at ease ordering wine with my dinner? And will I ever feel totally at ease with Paul's driving? I hope not!*

The lesson was now nearly over. *This is very useful to be learning the language here. This helps me understand how the people speak and it will help me understand their culture.* Is it possible to have strong understanding of a culture without having any knowledge of the language? One aspect of culture that his teacher, Pierre, had mentioned on the first day was that it was very important in France to begin conversations with a stranger with some kind of greeting. It was not recommended to merely start speaking to an unknown person without one. From this, he induced that France has a stricter, formal culture compared to back home. Thomas could think of countless times when he was walking around campus and people randomly came up to him and started speaking. Or sometimes they might begin the conversation with a "greeting", but it was a bit different than how Pierre was presenting the execution of French greetings. Frequently, a student might come up to him and merely say something like, "Hey man, where's the bookstore at?" This kind of greeting was very quick, and it was designed to get his attention more than to emphasize the greeting itself. Pierre was recommending a greeting that was more of an English equivalent of, "Good afternoon, sir, how are you?" The frequent French use of Madame (Mrs.) and Monsieur (Sir) was further evidence of French formalities. Thomas did remember having one high school classmate who had moved to Indiana from Georgia; this classmate addressed some of the older townspeople as "sir". But in the Midwest at least, this was exceptional, not the rule.

Thomas had also noticed during the grammar part of the lesson that the French had two forms of "you"; "vous" was more formal or for strangers, while "tu" was for familiar and more casual relationships. This was further evidence of a much stricter, more formal culture. The formal "you" did not seem to mesh well with the American way of life. The U.S. was a society that seemed to pride itself on a strong democratic ethos where everyone was supposedly equal. Purportedly, the U.S. was the "land of opportunity" where anyone could pull themselves up "by her bootstraps". Thomas knew that the realities of American life were far more complicated than these simple phrases, but at the same time, he could not imagine using a formal "you" tense back home. Culture in Indiana was largely casual, and this formality would certainly affect the ethos of cultural life.

"How was your first lesson of French?" Paul asked.

Thomas realized from his language study today why Paul had constructed his sentence that way. In French, constructions were often done in this manner: x of y rather than "French" modifying "lesson" as an adjective in the English style. *You can tell so much about a person's native language merely by listening to him speak English*, Thomas now perceived. Especially if he is not highly fluent, then it is likely that he will form sentences in a similar way to his native tongue. *I should pay close attention to all of the language mistakes that I hear while I am in France. This will help me understand how to become a better French speaker. The mistakes will highlight distinct French structures. Learning something from these mistakes that I hear will provide additional insight that goes beyond merely conjugating verbs and memorizing vocabulary.*

"I enjoyed it very much. I believe that studying French will make this experience much more meaningful," he replied.

"Good. Let's go home now."

During the walk back to the condo, Thomas also realized that he had a greater appreciation for French sounds as he heard chatter on the street. Of course he had also heard this chatter in the airport and around him before his first lesson, but it sounded much more like exotic noise to him at that point. Now he had spent some time seeing French words on paper and studying the pronunciation, he recognized more clearly some of the sounds that he was hearing. He realized more now why French was considered to be one of the "Romance languages". It did have somewhat of a romantic feel to it with relatively softer, pleasing sounds. He had only heard German briefly in some documentaries, but he did recall that these German sounds were much harder. Nobody in his right mind would ever call German a Romance language, he believed. *Not unless someone's idea of a romantic time was spitting on his date or taking a shower together and hacking saliva at each other.* This thought made Thomas recall the joke about the ideal European vacation vs. the worst one. In the ideal European vacation, you are greeted by a British person, a French person cooks for you, it is organized by a German, and you sleep with an Italian. The worst European vacation involves being greeted by a French person, a British person cooks for you, it is organized by an Italian, and you sleep with a German.

"Monday, you start to work at the hotel? Is it correct?" Paul asked.

"Yes, that is correct."

After they finished safely crossing the street, he had a sudden idea about what to ask him. *I should ask him why he hosts foreign students in his home. I am really curious, why did he want to host an American? If there is some kernel of truth to the joke about the vacation, then it implies that the French are not hospitable. Yet here I am in this situation, sleeping in a French family's home.*

"Am I the first foreigner that you've hosted in your home, Paul?"

"No. There were three others. We get about one each year."

"Why do you host people in your home?"

"It gives some variation to the daily flow of our life. I also like for my daughters to hear English at a young age. It is easier to learn another language when young."

Thomas looked extremely surprised to hear this response. His eyebrows perked up. "Couldn't you speak to your daughters sometimes in English if you wanted to?"

"Well, yes, of course, but they will just answer in French. If we have the foreign people in our home though, they are forced to hear the English much more."

Thomas hadn't considered this aspect of hosting foreigners. Apparently he was an English-speaking ambassador to the young girls.

Paul's comment also went against some stereotypes that Thomas had heard about the French. He had heard before that the French "didn't like the English language".

"Paul, do you think that it's good that English is so widespread around the world?"

Paul paused for thirty seconds, carefully considering how to respond. His eyes darkened a bit. "This question is complicated. Just like Americans, in France, we are not famous for speaking other languages. We have some second thoughts about so much English in Europe and other places. I read the news story about Chinese children preferring fried chicken to their own foods. This is not good. But we need to communicate with others when we travel. If I am in bad situation, bleeding, I hope that the medical people speak some English or French. If we cannot communicate, that is a very unpleasant situation. But we do not like Americans pushing their ways on us. As romantic, of course, I would like to see French have the position of English. But a man in Spain and Poland can say the same thing about their languages. The main idea, Thomas, is that I need to look at the world that my daughters are living in with some, how do you call it, practice, practical thinking. English will help them. If they know no English, it puts them in smaller position. Sorry, Thomas, I wish that I had learned more English when I was a student. I could speak much better at this situation with you. I cannot speak well in English compared to French. I feel limit on how to put my thoughts to you. The main idea I am trying to say is I need to look at our world as is, not as some romantic dreamer. It is easier to be a dreamer when young. I need to see the world as is more now; I have a family. Do you understand my thought?"

"Yes, I do. I sought out this experience in France because I felt so limited in my university environment. You see English as helping your daughters grow in some way. I feel the same about learning French and seeing another culture. Most of my classmates in school just see the world through their eyes or contacts. I want to see it more through a telescope. I don't mean that I am traveling to space, but I want to see the larger picture. I heard that the U.S. has about five percent of the world's population. I am inclined to think that those other ninety-five percent have something to teach me. If you are moving through a large buffet at a restaurant and the food is delicious, aren't you missing something by only trying one or two dishes?"

"We are told that the Americans like to eat big plates of food," Paul replied.

"Well, yes, Paul. I can look at it from the perspective of my waistline or from the perspective of experience. I think that sometimes a big meal with several dishes can be a positive experience. Most people are not going to travel all the time. Travel would lose its thrill if it is done constantly. Likewise, it would not be as exciting to eat a buffet every day. When done sporadically, it offers a greater breadth of flavors, just as international travel does."

"This could be true, but I enjoy the most eating French food. The flavors of other foods feel strange."

"Well, Paul, this might be how a lot of people feel about travel in general. Possibly they *enjoy* staying at home the most. It is probably uncomfortable when they travel to other countries. Do you think that I feel completely comfortable here? How do you think that I felt when the waiter looked in horror at me when I wanted to have an apple juice with my dinner? But don't these uncomfortable experiences force us to stretch ourselves a bit more? Short-term discomfort can lead to long-term gain. I remember when one of my college classmates told me how much he enjoyed his deep tissue massages. He said that he had some pain during the massage, but then he felt great during the next few days. The short-term pain helps him reach his longer-term goals of a more flexible, healthier body. If someone wants to be completely relaxed all the time on a beach with no stress and no discomfort, I do not see how this person matures and grows over time."

"I see what you are trying to say. I would like to be more open to some other foods, but it is difficult for me. I hope that my daughters can learn to appreciate other cuisines. Possibly if they embark on an experience that is similar to what you are doing now in France, this can help them in this goal. I struggle with my habits, Thomas."

"We all do, Paul. At least you recognize that you have a struggle about being closed to many kinds of foods. Most of the people that I've met in my hometown or at my university have no conception whatsoever that their perspectives are limited or narrow. They have no desire to broaden their mindsets; they do not see any problem that exists. Recognizing a problem is a very large first step. The possibility for improvement is infinitely greater when a person recognizes a weakness. During this conversation, at least I feel as though we are on a similar plane. I do not feel that we are talking past each other. If I tried to have this conversation with most of the people in my hometown, I would feel that we were completely talking over each other. We might be speaking the same language literally, but it would not feel that way. It is similar to when there is a debate about the existence of God between a very religious person and an atheist or agnostic. Most of the time, they are just talking past one another. The religious person sees the world in a completely different manner than the atheist. Their metaphysical conceptions are incompatible with each other, and therefore, the conversation feels largely pointless and devoid of substance."

"Yes, you have many more religious people in America than we have in France."

"True. I think that my previous comments summarize well

the alienation that I experienced as a university student and high school student. I felt as though I were on a different plane than almost everyone else. This isolated intellectual feeling is what caused my angst and suffering. It is critical that we can speak with others who understand us. It isn't fundamental that they understand us one hundred percent or that they agree with us about everything. But being able to speak with other people who are on the same level as us intellectually is necessary. Very few of us can survive completely alone on an island, literally or intellectually."

"You are in a good place if you enjoy discussing the ideas, Thomas. We have discussed many in our cafés through the centuries," Paul said with another slight wink.

Thomas could not remember which condo was his "home". The experience so far of being in a foreign land felt like one of constant bombardment to the senses. Every aspect of his existence here was different than at home. All of these adjustments and unique experiences were stimulating but also made him feel much more exhausted than usual. His body clock was still on American time, and it felt suitable to fall asleep for the evening, even though it was dinner time. The condos appeared to be remarkably uniform in his mental state of exhaustion, and if Paul had not been with him, he would have had no clue which one to enter. *Randomly knocking on each door until I find the right one might not be the ideal approach. They are not armed here with guns, assault weapons, and possibly bazookas or nukes as they are in Indiana. But if I knock on a stranger's door and I only am able to speak a few words of French, then that could be a recipe for disaster. I might learn a plethora of French swear words, but at what cost? No, I had enough scowls for a month at the restaurant.*

They entered his "home" and Thomas immediately could tell

from the smells that Marie was cooking up a storm. Often when he entered basic restaurants in Indiana, he could recognize the smells quite easily. It was simple food, and it was obvious what the smell was. He had noticed that a lot of the sauces and garnishes in France were quite elaborate. Their complex compositions made it more difficult to decipher the components of the smell. *Well, I don't know what I smell, but it smells wonderful. I would pay money at home just to smell this, much less eat it! If we usually have to pay money to eat food, why are smells always free? Smells of this quality surely must have some monetary value.*

He could already hear French people saying to him, "If you Americans had proper noses, wouldn't you recognize the slop of what you are eating? These burgers and fries oozing with grease; you call this food? The Neanderthals in caves ate more elegantly than you scoundrels. Just drink the fertilizer straight from the bottle instead of putting it in your fast food; save yourself the trouble. It's more efficient." *I often do feel borderline sick when I am done eating a fast food meal,* Thomas conceded to these French thoughts. *Would it feel that much different if I actually drank part of a bottle of fertilizer? I am not going to scientifically test this, but it is an interesting hypothetical question to ponder.*

Thomas rubbed his hands together and asked Paul, "What are we eating for dinner tonight?" Eating in France wasn't just an activity of basic sustenance. It was more similar to a full-fledged culinary ball. Maslow's hierarchy of needs would place traditional eating as a basic physiological need. It seemed to be an activity here that greatly exceeded the mere physiological. Maslow's higher order needs that Thomas had learned about referred to "esteem needs" and the highest one was referred to as "self-actualization": when a person was close to achieving full potential. *I don't know exactly where I would put eating in France on this pyramid. But I certainly feel like a full, enriched human being when I eat these elaborately prepared, exquisite meals. Eating here is, at a minimum, an esteem need. During its best moments, it gives the impression of full self-actualization. If by some stretch of the imagination, religious people are correct and there is a Heaven, they had better serve French food*, Thomas thought. *Heaven without these French dishes is a heaven in name only. It would also be fundamental for this Heaven to have bottomless butter available with no cardiological consequences. Just give us a second heart when the first one fails from the bottomless butter. Poof!*

If Heaven exists, then Hell probably exists too. They probably serve French people American food all the time in Hell. I do not know what else could torment them more for their transgressions. To eat food that is below Neanderthal, yes, that is a suitable punishment in Hell for a French person.

Through the haze of these thoughts, Thomas heard the answer to his question about dinner: "Filet mignon with onion soup and salad." *Right, it's time to switch back to reality instead of pondering the afterlife of butter swimming pools. If there were butter swimming pools, would one section be cordoned off as the "I can't believe it's not butter section"? Definitely there would not be a margarine pool though; that would not be fit for Heaven. In Hell, one might find this on the other hand? Possibly. When you move up to purgatory though, at least the margarine pools would be trans-fat-free.*

Returning to reality, the thought of having filet mignon for dinner made Thomas's heart race. He had eaten this dish once in his entire lifetime. *The dish does sound rather French now that I think about it*, Thomas realized. *I had never made the connection before. English has so many words that are of foreign origin that it becomes problematic to make all of the connections successfully. It would be almost as arduous as endeavoring to learn all of the foreign languages of the world. It is tempting to make a stronger French connection with French fries or French toast, even though those dishes have nothing to do with France! Filet mignon, on the other hand, doesn't immediately "scream" as a French dish because beef in and of itself is a somewhat ordinary food. This is just a fancier version of beef. That is what makes it "more French".*

He was also going to be eating onion soup for dinner. *I have never heard of onion soup. I have had French onion soup though before. Wait a minute; this is French onion soup! They don't call it that because we're in France. Just as beef in an American restaurant is not labeled as "American beef"; it's redundant. Will I be able to handle eating both filet mignon and French onion soup at the same meal? This sounds incredibly appetizing. French onion soup usually has a very strong smell; surely that was the majority of what I smelled when I came in. Filet mignon is an amazing dish, but it does not evoke the same aromas as French onion soup.*

Twenty minutes later, the meal began. Marie served a light rosé wine to go with the meal. Thomas decided to drink some. *I am going to adapt to French life bit by bit. It is not realistic to adapt immediately to everything at the beginning of a foreign experience. My adaptation here will be piecemeal. I am beginning to learn French and now attempting to have a glass of wine with my dinner. It feels abnormal to drink wine with my dinner; however, if I do not, I receive tacit disapproval and puzzled stares. The mild discomfort of following a custom that I am not at ease with is better than these powerful stares that come from not following the custom.*

He was starting to realize that there are a large number of decisions during the course of foreign travel that have these outcomes. *I will have to constantly weigh the difficulty of performing an unaccustomed act with the unpleasantness of clashing with the culture and standing out as someone who is not in the know. Foreign travel, generally speaking, is a bit like wearing an uncomfortable pair of shoes. In some places, it is analogous to a slightly uncomfortable pair, and elsewhere, it is equivalent to an extremely uncomfortable pair of shoes that is three sizes too big. Much growth and development can result from these experiences, but I have to be willing to wear the shoes that don't fit.*

When Thomas asked Paul to pour him a glass of wine, Marie's face lit up. However, Paul had his usual fairly stoic expression, and the two young daughters of course were indifferent to Thomas's actions. *In their world, I am just a strange man taking up space in a room in their house. I would have had the same reaction if there had been a "long-term" guest in my home when I was young. Hopefully though, they do not confuse me with someone who is homeless.*

The food at this meal was a notable contrast to his first dinner in the restaurant. The restaurant meal, although it was extremely tasty, had more of a "restaurant flavor". Thomas could taste much more butter in the food at the restaurant. Marie's meal, on the other hand, tasted "home cooked". She still had added a somewhat buttery sauce to the filet mignon, which seemed to be a consistent feature of French cooking. But the food had a lighter feel to it overall. The onion soup was elaborately seasoned as well. Thomas ate slowly, savoring the taste of each bite. *I would give anything to have home cooking in my family of this quality.* He had noticed that Marie had labored in the kitchen for a quite significant period of time to prepare the meal. His mother at home usually prepared quick, convenient meals. He believed that it required discipline and commitment to spend this much time cooking. *But it also seems to be a cultural expectation over here. Quick and convenient meals seem to be scorned and poorly regarded.* Most likely, from a young age, Marie knew that she would be expected to labor long hours in the kitchen for her future family. She witnessed her mother performing these activities and accepted that eventually she too would be subject to the same expectations.

Our family environments certainly have a strong influence on us. How much free will do we have to forge our own path in life? The influence of parents is not exactly analogous to a rigid solid, with no opportunity for deviation. If that were true, I would not be in France right now, Thomas reasoned. *However, parental influence cannot be analogous to a gas either, where it is effortless to completely escape from all of their teachings and "evaporate away". No, it is analogous to some form of matter that is in between the two. A stretchable ball of putty might be an apt comparison. The putty has a basic structure that is influenced by the parents, with some abilities to stretch and move onto a different path.* He considered the possibility that some French wives (and in rarer cases, husbands) do fix quick and simple meals. Among the millions of wives in France, are there any who prepare quick meals? Most likely, there are some. But if they grew up with these cultural influences, possibly they would feel a stronger sense of guilt if they spent less time preparing meals? An American wife (or husband) would simply see the convenient cooking as normal. Thomas thought that it was probable that the French person would feel significantly more guilt and anxiety about this action. In a culture that reveres food so much as an art form, this action would feel tantamount to failure and inferiority. *In any case, I am quite fortunate to be staying in a home where the wife does prepare exquisite meals. I am one of the beneficiaries of this toil. I have the privilege of eating five-star quality meals during my stay.*

Paul commented about his work assignment, lifting Thomas out of his reverie.

"In two days, I understand that you begin the work at the hotel. This hotel is not far from your language school. Do you know what you are doing at this hotel?"

"I will be a bellhop."

"Quoi...eh, I mean, I do not know this word," Paul replied.

"A bellhop carries luggage to and from rooms. I believe that I may be assisting with room service as well."

"I see. We call that porteur in French."

"That sounds similar to a porter, so it makes sense. We basically have the same word in English; we just don't say it as romantically as the French do."

Paul's eyebrows moved 45 degrees after hearing this comment and he smirked a little bit.

"Thomas, you find us to be romantic already? Has a French girl kissed you in such short time?"

"Only in my dreams last night. Even deeper romance has taken place in my dreams every night. I have had the dream equivalent of a French kiss."

"This is not the same," Paul replied with a look of utter seriousness. His countenance looked quite puzzled. "Do you see a romantic as someone who can dream? Then it is easy to be the romantic."

"It is not just about dreams, Paul. France feels romantic to me. Eating an exquisite meal with fine wine is romantic. Walking by beautiful historical buildings from the Roman era is romantic. Your language sounds romantic with its sonorous sounds. Why does romance have to be confined to kissing and other such activities?"

"I do not say that romance is only kissing. But you have stayed here for a couple of days. That is too short be using this word romance. A man has to work for romance, Thomas. Maybe because of the youth, you think that the romance comes served on plate of gold. No, romance is more of a result after climbing the long mountain. After wanting to give up during the climb and getting hurt during the climb. After all of this has happened, then possibly it is romance. You have developed the impression too easily, I believe."

Thomas felt that that Paul was stretching his words out of context. He mainly meant it as a joke that the French said the word "porter" more romantically; few associate romantic images with being a porter or bellhop. One sly comment developed into this convoluted discussion about what it means to be a romantic. But Thomas was not resentful. He had constantly complained in the past about the glibness of the conversations around him. At least Paul was trying to engage him. Thomas sensed that Paul was caricaturing his behavior as very American. Here was this superficial, easily impressed American who saw romance as analogous to instant coffee, while Paul, the enlightened Frenchman, knew that romance meant slowly roasting the beans before drinking the coffee. Thomas was also beginning to think that he was overreacting to Paul's comments. Possibly Paul was merely trying to have a thought-provoking discussion, and Thomas was interpreting the comments much too personally.

Additionally, if I am able to present myself as an intellectual with a thick skin who is not easily offended, then possibly Paul will develop a more positive impression of my nation. Even if Paul does have certain preconceptions about Americans, first, I cannot entirely blame him. Second, these impressions are not fixed in stone. I want Paul to at least have a positive impression of me as a thoughtful American; this is the first step towards giving him a nuanced impression of my nation.

Thomas further reflected that Paul's comments about romance

were worthwhile to stew over for at least a couple of hours. He had never discussed this particular issue before. He had never wondered if "temporary romance" could exist. Maybe easy, instant romance was more of a dream than a feature of the real world. He certainly could not point to many experiences in the "real world" where he had found romance easily. Sure, he had immensely enjoyed his two French dinners. But didn't Paul have a point that this was perverting the idea of romance to call these experiences by this name? He *loved* the food, and it gave him immense pleasure, but surely, pleasure and romance were not synonymous? Pleasure might indeed be a necessary condition for romance, but it seemed to stretch plausibility that it was a sufficient condition. Something else needed to be boiling in the romantic stew.

A couple of days later, Thomas began his work at the hotel. It was a picturesque, traditional French hotel that had high ceilings and oak furniture. He saw sofas that appeared to be fit for Napoleon; they were spacious and their colors brightened nicely from the sun's rays through the window during the daytime. He had learned in his French class that, in French, the fine arts were called the "beautiful arts", which highlighted their high importance in French culture. He also felt a sense of artistry in the decorations and atmosphere of the hotel. The lobby was carefully decorated to evoke beauty. A large part of the lobby had pleasing shades of color: the ceiling had numerous bright Impressionist paintings. Below the ceiling, lovely combinations of orange and yellow complemented the paintings.

Although it was true that Thomas had read a newspaper article suggesting that the French on the whole could be perceived as a "gloomy" nation with high levels of depression, it was nonetheless quite clear that public spaces and hotels had a pleasing external appearance. Thomas had read another article arguing that there was a tremendous amount of research that suggested a link between creativity and depression. The article argued that the research suggested that creative people were likely to think more, and therefore, they were more likely to become depressed. This made sense to Thomas. Certainly he had experienced his own struggles with depression from a mind that was in constant motion and reflection. Many of his simpler classmates in college were quite content merely to party four or five nights a week. If they were able to be drunk consistently and attend loud parties, then this was happiness for them. There were days that Thomas envied that simplicity of needs and desires. He did not envy the livers of these classmates, nor the productivity that they lost from being sick and vomiting from drinking. But he did see some minute benefit to gaining pleasure so easily rather than pushing against waves of alienation that at times could feel like a tsunami.

His first day of work was fairly unremarkable. He didn't expect that working as a bellhop was going to be a highly exhilarating experience, but Thomas did have one unusual customer. The man was waiting in the lobby with a few bags, huffing and puffing after his entrance into the hotel. He reeked of cigarette smoke, and he had a surly, irritated countenance. When the man saw him, he shouted something at him in French. Thomas replied, in French, that he only spoke a little French, and then said "sorry" in English. The man met his words with more shouting. Thomas walked over to Jean, his supervisor, whom he had met a couple of hours ago.

"What is this man shouting about?" he asked.

"Zis man is upset that you work here and do not speak the French. He says that foreigners are destroying French traditions, and the hotel should not hire people who do not speak our language. But he said that you are better than the Algerians. Maybe you will see some customers like this man," Jean replied in a matter-of-fact tone.

"Tell him that I love French toast topped with French fries. Perhaps that will calm him down," Thomas said.

Jean looked quite baffled. "I do not understand. In French, just telling him that you like fries will not stop the shouting. This man has hot temper."

"That's why I would like to explain to him that I like hot food, Jean. This man likes hot things. His temper is hot. He likes to put some spice and garnishes into his tone of voice. If he knows that I eat hot French toast with burnt French fries on top, maybe he will see that we can become buddies, in a hot kind of way. Do you follow me, Jean?"

"No."

After his comment, Jean's facial expression reminded Thomas of something; it was an eerie feeling of déjà vu. He wondered where he had seen this expression before. He then realized it was quite similar to how the waiter stared at him when he ordered apple juice in the restaurant instead of wine. It was that "Are you from Planet Earth or Neptune?" look. *Maybe I should go easy on the sarcasm during my first day of work. Sure, this is not my career, and it's just a temporary job. But I do not want to get fired before my stay concludes in France. He probably does not speak enough English to understand my jokes. Even people in Indiana often find my humor a bit off-putting*, Thomas remembered, *and they were native speakers. So how can I expect this French man with limited English to understand what the hell I am talking about? I do miss being around people who speak my language.*

There is something to be said for people who know the hills

and valleys of your language. Thomas remembered a discussion during a college class about "outside-in" concepts versus "inside-out" concepts. He now realized that a person's native language is very much "inside-out". *I just "know" the language without having to think deeply about how to speak. My privileged position on the inside allows for quite bounteous possibilities with regard to expression, comprehension, and humor. Speaking a foreign language and being in a foreign country, on the other hand, are very much "outside-in". I am looking at everything from the periphery or possibly even further away. Everything feels just a bit off. Pronouncing the words and conjugating the verbs does not feel normal or customary. Especially in the beginning stages, it can feel as if I am attempting to become something that I am not. My tongue is attempting to get around sounds that it is not conditioned to speak.*

Likewise, the experience of a foreign land replicates the "outside-in" feeling. I am unfamiliar with many of the customs and traditions. I do not know how to behave "properly" in many situations. I am also more likely to be viewed with suspicion; this happened today with this yelling and screaming man. It is akin to trying on clothes that just do not quite seem to fit. I can make an adjustment here in my belt buckle, have a tailor make a few trimmings, but still the clothes do not feel right.

Has my alienation really improved by coming to France? Yes, I have enjoyed some of these deeper discussions that I have had and the food has been fabulous. But they do not speak my language, and therefore, usually cannot understand my jokes. It is also often in the back of my mind that everything I do may be understood to represent "American" behavior even if has nothing to do with mainstream Americans and is just an expression of my individual personality. I want to feel part of some kind of a community, but am having serious doubts that any such feeling will develop during my stay in France.

To be screamed at in a foreign language that I speak poorly is a quite unique feeling of disaffection. Yes, my parents sometimes screamed at me during childhood in some of our darker moments. But I understood what they were screaming about. To hear screams in a foreign tongue represents a different order of magnitude. It helps when someone is screaming at me to know what they are saying. Are they saying that they are going to kill me? Are they saying that my service is bad? Or are they saying that their ham sandwich should have had Grey Poupon instead of runny mustard? Those three declarations all have extremely different meanings and consequences, but because I am an outsider here, I do not know what he was saying. I had to rely on a translation from my supervisor. Certainly this is better than no information whatsoever, but the translator can spin the expressions towards his own interpretation and preconceived notions. He can also omit part of what was said. What if, by remote chance, the man had said that he was going to kill me? Jean might not have mentioned this to avoid scaring me off from this job. It is very unlikely that the man said this. But it is frustrating not to know myself exactly what he said. All that I have is Jean's spin. This is an incomplete rendering of the man's screams.

It is almost as if I am starting over again as a child here. "Daddy, what did the man say? Why is he screaming at me?" A child also does not know the proper etiquette in many situations. Likewise, many people are annoyed by young children in various situations: the child bawling in the restaurant, the children who are horsing around and interfering with serious pursuits in a museum or bookstore. So I spent several hours on a plane just to become a child again? It was not satisfactory to be a native-speaking adult in my homeland. I disliked many of the customs at home, but I understood what the customs were. I knew the rules of the game; I just didn't like the rules! Isn't that still better than being ignorant of the rules themselves?

3

Chapter Three

September 2015

During the next few months, Thomas returned for many more shifts at the hotel. He did not experience another customer who was as extreme as the yelling and screaming gentleman, but he did perceive a lot of brusqueness in customers that he assisted. Many customers stopped speaking to him after they picked up that he was foreign and made no effort to say "thank you". He did not feel much gratitude from most of the customers. True, he had not given much thought to hotel bellhops in the United States either. *Perhaps it is a good experience to walk in their shoes. Yes, it is a basic job. But it makes the difference between a mediocre day at work and a respectable one to experience that at least one customer is thankful for my assistance.*

The French are no doubt a highly intellectual people, but Thomas believed that they came up short when it comes to everyday graciousness. *I used to think that being intellectual was the "be all and end all" of my existence. I thought that if that component of my life was fulfilled, then I would be completely satisfied. I have been able to experience numerous great intellectual conversations during my stay here, yet I feel that something else is missing. I do miss having a couple of American customers who earnestly and enthusiastically thank me for my help. I might even smile a little bit if someone wished me a great day. It becomes trite to hear "have a great day" constantly in Indiana, yet when I never hear it, I also feel that something is lost.* He did not want twenty customers at the hotel each day to wish him a great day. He wanted one or two. Yet this kind of greeting or expression simply was not part of the culture in Bordeaux.

The image of the flowing river entered his mind. You can move to a different place in the river and gain something, but you will always lose something as well. He also believed that it was not just merely a case of wanting to hear "have a nice day" from someone. These expressions in the U.S., although they felt stale in excess, were symptoms of a more positive spirit. He did perceive a strong presence of gloom among a significant percentage of the population in Bordeaux. He was nostalgic for some American optimism that tomorrow would be a better day than today. *I have struggled with my own gloomy thoughts for most of my life, and it does not help matters to feel them in so many others here. It tends to compound my gloom further.*

My realization that I have not found a paradise here continues this ethos of gloom. In many respects, my mental state has not changed from college in Indiana. There, I missed stimulating conversations. Here, I miss gratitude, cheerfulness, and meeting a lot of people who speak my language well and who might understand my jokes. In both situations, there is a strong feeling that I am lacking something. Rather than solving my problems, I have merely moved them to a different place.

Yet Thomas did not have a single ounce of regret that he had decided to come to France. He was reminded of some people saying that it was better to have relationships with women that failed than never to have any relationships at all. Likewise, he felt that it was far superior to experience something novel and reach these conclusions rather than spend the rest of his life wondering what it might have been like if he had decided to have an exotic experience. *If I had not come here, I would still have these delusions that France is a paradise, and that would not be a superior position. No, that would be far worse. Furthermore, I always despised any and all American optimism. That has now evolved into a more complex position and I will benefit from this more nuanced thinking when I return to Indiana. It won't destroy my spirits as much if I feel an intellectual loneliness, as long as I can find something else worthwhile to balance it out.*

I am beginning to see the world in much greater shades of gray. Possibly not fifty shades of gray yet, but at least in single digits, and that is a leap from my prior thinking. I now realize how much travel changes the eyes. Of course, it does not literally change my eyes. My vision does not change. But what is processed through these eyes is enormously affected by travel. The non-traveler is more likely to simply see red, blue, and green. But the traveler, from being in so many uncomfortable situations that rocked his foundations, sees not only red, but ten different shades of red. The traveler can distinguish kelly green from dark green, and this distinction has great meaning. For the non-traveler, green is simply green. The non-traveler has never been forced to probe these more subtle hues of green.

Five years from now, if I am sitting enjoying a beer in Indiana, am I still going to be upset that I didn't feel enough gratitude when I worked as a bellhop? Of course not! Will I still be upset that a waiter was horrified that I did not order wine, or that some people did not understand my jokes? Certainly not! But I will be extremely appreciative of these bigger eyes that I now have. The traveler has a privileged lens on the world. It is very important for me to keep this at the center of my thinking. I do not think that this will be my only travel experience before I return to Indiana. That would almost seem to contradict everything that I have been thinking today. If it is true that this experience has given me bigger eyes, why would I want to stop now? Wouldn't it follow that I would want my eyes to grow again? If it is true that I see colors before that did not exist in my psyche, why depart from that path? Surely, I do not see all of the colors yet! That would be impossible after merely one travel experience. Undoubtedly, there are myriad more colors that I cannot perceive yet because I have experienced such a limited portion of the flowing river that we call this planet.

As he walked home from his hotel shift, Thomas clearly saw that he had not fully resolved his feelings about the benefits and burdens of travel. There was only one solution, and that was to continue traveling. In many respects, this time in France had opened up a Pandora's box of endless possibility. Rather than merely fulfilling a very limited goal, it had transported him into an entirely different mental realm and now he wanted that realm to grow exponentially. If a person only has one extended travel experience and then they stop traveling, are they a real traveler? *Most likely not*, Thomas thought. This would be more of a case of someone trying the "travel thing" and then finding that they are not a fit; they find instead that they are much more well-suited to standard, pedestrian life in the motherland. Thomas did consider himself to be a real traveler though, which was why he knew that this was definitely not the end of this prolonged journey. He thought of Donald Rumsfeld's famous quote about known unknowns and unknown unknowns. *I both know and do not know what I do not know.* He knew that the range of countries and possible experiences that went along with these different countries was virtually limitless. He just did not know how all of those different experiences would further transform him. If he had traveled enough, would he have been so bothered by Paul's driving when he had first arrived in France? Furthermore, would long plane rides irritate him so much if he had traveled more? Thomas did not know.

My work visa will be expiring in a few weeks. I need to determine where my next destination is going to be. Coming to France was a big jump from Indiana. Now where would be another large jump? I do not want to continue exploring Europe for now. I feel pretty satisfied with my experience with both my host family and to a more limited extent with my language school classmates. I have walked by countless cathedrals and seen numerous historical buildings. My practical experience of history has vastly improved, but I do not feel that it would be the best use of limited time to have another in-depth European experience right now. Remembering comedic impressions of George H. W. Bush on YouTube, Thomas felt that more European travel would "not be prudent at this juncture". The French breathe their history in this land. They exhale vapors of freedom and liberty just as their ancestors did during the French Revolution. They sit in cafés discussing philosophy and literature, just as their ancestors did in the salon culture of a few previous centuries. *I feel immense joy that I have been able to almost feel that history with my fingertips and not merely read about it in a history text in a library cubicle. But it would violate my travel principles to keep treading European water. I will maximize my stimulation more if I experience another continent and its culture. But where should I go?*

This was the subject of his next dinner with his host family.

He knew that he would be leaving France within a month, and because of this, he tried to savor every bit of Marie's cooking. *Will I ever again have such easy access to French food? Will I ever again be in a situation where I can merely roll out of bed and smell the love of French cuisine?* He wondered if there were any French restaurants in the entire state of Indiana. *Could a French restaurant do well back home? Possibly they would have to serve the wine in beer glasses to cater to the locals. Otherwise, the wine would not sell. Would they "McDonald's-ize" the fries with extra sugar and nuclear waste as well? Yes, this possibly is an opportunity that will never again be duplicated in my life. My future consumption of French food most likely will be few and far between, and it is very unlikely that the quality will be comparable.* Thomas realized that this thought neatly captured the concept of *carpe diem*, especially as it was demonstrated in *Dead Poets Society*. When Mr. Keating was discussing "seizing the day", it was all about capturing that specific moment. Don't let the day roll over you; you yourself need to seize it.

Thomas wanted to hear the family's feedback about where he should travel next. During dinner, he asked what they thought. Part of the conversation took place in French.

Paul replied that he thought that he should look at another country in Europe.

"Why do you think so, Paul?"

"This continent has much. You say that you like the history, and there is more to see."

"Will the food be as good if I go to another European country?" Thomas asked.

Upon hearing this comment, Marie nearly jumped out of her chair. Generally, she had been giving him much more cheerful vibes now that she could speak mostly French to him; there had been some small gravitational drops in aloofness. She replied in French, "You came here just for the food?"

"Not just for the food. It was ninety-five percent for the food and five percent for pleasing cigarette smoke."

Marie still had not warmed up to his attempts at humor. "We are not proud of our smoking. I never heard of someone coming to my country to experience that. You can smell cigarette smoke in your country, yes?"

"But it's not the same. At home, the cigarette smoke is surrounded by farms. Its smell tends to mix more with manure. Here the cigarette smoke tastes much more buttery and full of sauce, just like the food."

Marie grimaced at hearing these comments. Her nose crinkled and her facial expression turned to a frown in response. "You should not compare cigarette smoke to French food. We have some bad habits here in France of smoking a lot. We are not perfect, but it is an insult to our cuisine to say that the cigarette smoke tastes French to you."

"I'm sorry, Marie. You know that I have loved your cooking. I've mentioned it many times. I was trying to be funny, but I think that I missed the mark."

"Yes, Thomas, I understand. Making jokes about someone's culture is a delicate art, not radically different from a finely prepared French meal. It requires thought and planning and careful consideration. If you just say whatever is first in your head, it often will miss the mark. It would be similar to the case of a fine French chef preparing a meal with no planning, as if he just threw a bunch of random ingredients together impulsively. If you want to be funny, it needs to follow more of a process."

Thomas was not quite sure about Marie's analogy here. Humor was spontaneous, by its very nature. He thought that if anyone gave too much thought to a joke, something would be lost.

"Seriously, is there anywhere else in Europe where I will enjoy the food so much?" Thomas asked.

"Possibly in Italy. If this is your main priority, then you should go there next," Paul replied.

"My impulse tells me that I want to experience something more different than another European country. I want a second travel experience that will shake my foundations a bit more than merely going to Italy next," Thomas replied.

"I do not know if I can offer you useful advice then, Thomas," Paul said slowly in French. "I have not traveled outside of Europe much other than a cruise on some Caribbean islands when Marie and I were younger. Perhaps you should look in the travel section of a bookstore. Especially in Paris, they have some large bookstores with English sections if you would like to explore this topic in your language. I recommend that you take the train to Paris. You have not experienced our trains much. That alone will add to your experience. As much as I love my city and prefer to live here rather than Paris, it would also be worthwhile for you to sightsee in our capital before you leave, even if their wines are significantly inferior to ours," he noted with his slight grin.

This is definitely a culture that has tremendous pride in its wine. Paul has the confidence to say that one of the world's most famous capitals has inferior wine to his city! Wine seems to be a huge component of his identity as a Bordeaux-ian. Interesting that he was taken aback a bit when I said that I came to France for the food, but he has no qualms about discussing wine as part of his identity. It is true, though, that Bordeaux is particularly famous for wine. What other aspect of his city could he plausibly claim was superior to Paris? It makes sense that he would cling to a famous aspect of his smaller city when trying to compare it to a behemoth such as Paris.

There is a natural tendency for people to feel inferior or sensitive when discussing a smaller city compared to a famous capital. Of course he is going to bring up Bordeaux's chief claim to fame! It is healthy, though, for a person to have a reasonable amount of pride in his hometown. If the pride is based on a legitimate source (in this case, it was wine), then he should feel proud of where he has grown up. There is no intrinsic reason to loathe where we are from. I am filled with negative emotions about my hometown from my experiences growing up, but it would certainly be better if I were able to see a glass that is somewhat full. I am quite the expert on feeling alienated! What a beautiful contrast it would be to experience the opposite sentiment. It almost sounds comparable to a dream at this point in my life.

Thomas decided that he would follow Paul's suggestion to travel to Paris. He still had not experienced the capital, and an internationally oriented bookstore sounded like a great suggestion. When he had looked at his current program on campus at the International Programs office, the advisor working there recommended that he do the program in a smaller city in France rather than in Paris. The advisor said that he would see the true culture of the country much more in a smaller city, away from the hustle and bustle of a hectic, gigantic capital. Thomas had followed this advice, and by and large, he agreed with it. But at the same time, he felt that he should at least experience Paris for a few days before leaving the country. It was equally important to experience the center of economic and cultural life in France, even if their wines were obviously inferior in Paul's totally objective opinion. *Maybe they compensate by having better quality apple juice. What could be more romantic than a fine bottle of apple juice?*

The next day, he packed up his bags and headed over to the

Bordeaux train station. This would be his first train experience in France. Up to this point, he had only been on a domestic flight and traveled around in Paul's (quasi) race car. Thomas waited in line to purchase his ticket for the three-and-a-half-hour train journey. He was now able to accomplish this task in French. The man at the station selling tickets asked if he wanted tickets for "fumeur" or "non-fumeur". At first, Thomas associated this question with English too much, wondering why he would want a section where people fume and scream at him like the angry customer at the hotel. Then he remembered from his French lessons that fumeur meant to smoke.

The conversation came back to him in which the instructor asked them about their smoking habits. Jinsei, who had struggled to learn French compared to the others, managed to put together a sentence that he smoked about twenty-five cigarettes a day. That comment then reminded Jinsei that he had only smoked five cigarettes so far that day, and he promptly left the room to go have a smoke. He did say that he was "very, very sorry", though, to leave in the middle of class. *I suppose that as long as you say that you're very, very sorry, then any behavior is permissible.* Just as Dostoyevsky was attributed as saying some variation of "without God, everything is permitted", the equivalent in this discussion was "as long as I say that I am more than just very sorry, everything is permitted". On some level, Thomas felt as if he had stumbled on a conceptual equivalency between a godless world and being very, very sorry. Clearly, remorse increases significantly when God goes out the window.

Without any hesitation, Thomas chose the non-screaming, non-smoking section. He answered a few more questions, and then the employee virtually threw the ticket at him. Again, Thomas felt nostalgic for American-style customer service. *At least wish me a nice afternoon when you throw the ticket at me. It will help lessen the blow to know that you'd still like for me to have a nice day despite the fact that that you throw paper objects at me.*

He was impressed at the efficiency of the operations in the train station though. The tracks were in good condition, and the trains appeared to be very well maintained. The trains also seemed to run on schedule as well. As he boarded his clean and well-maintained train, his eyes sparkled from the comfortable seats compared to the long flight across the Atlantic. *This ride will also hopefully provide an opportunity to see some greenery in the countryside. Perhaps I can observe some areas where this legendary French wine is grown.*

He sat down next to a middle-aged man who was engrossed in reading some kind of long novel. A few minutes later, the man said something to him in French at a very fast speed, so Thomas did not understand what he was saying. He replied that he only spoke a bit of French. Upon hearing this, the man crinkled his nose, frowned, and continued reading.

Paul has the facial expressions of a saint compared to this man. Those faint smiles seem infinitely friendlier than this man's massive frowns that accompany his clenched nose. I am tempted to tell him just to blow his nose rather than clenching it so much. Don't let those nasal passages be a victim to your snobbery; just blow it out onto a tissue. However, I do not speak French well enough to be able to put together this thought. I suppose that I looked at many of my college classmates in a similar manner. It feels quite different when the shoe is on the other foot! But was I wrong to look down on a lot of my classmates? Should I respect that they had no interest in learning or intellectually enriching themselves?

Seeing that conversation was not going to be the prime focus of the journey, Thomas mostly stared out the window. He was indeed impressed by the French countryside. He saw beautiful, well-maintained farms and enchanting-looking vineyards. He observed workers farming the land with great care. This is the original source of their food and wine. It makes sense that they would have tremendous pride in this process. As he passed by one farm, the look on the farmer's face communicated the thought: "This land means everything to me. I eat, breathe, and sleep for this farm. I value the food that is produced from this farm as much as I value my wife and my family."

Thomas had thought that he could no longer be impressed by the food culture in France. He thought that he had reached the saturation point and that the astonishing quality of the food simply seemed "normal" to him. But the experience of passing by the farms and vineyards from the train added another dimension to his admiration. *There is something very wholesome about their food culture. We have "industrialized" food so much in the U.S. with all of the processed foods and ubiquitous fast food, but they have stayed pure on a completely different level. We tend to desire things that are cheap, fast, and easy back in the United States, and sometimes, this can be virtuous. I love being able to shop on Amazon so conveniently. But this principle has unquestionably gone too far with our food practices. The French see their food as an extension of their souls. We need more of that in my country.*

Eventually, he fell asleep. He realized that he had been sleeping for quite some time since the train was very close to arriving in Paris. The snooty man fired off several sentences in French at him when he saw that Thomas had woken up. But, of course, Thomas had no clue what the man was saying. *Possibly I was snoring? Possibly I invaded his space when I fell asleep? I have definitely been exposed to a lot of angry French people between this man and the raving lunatic at the hotel. French may be a beautiful language, but it seems to lose quite a bit of its luster when they are screaming it at me. Something definitely cannot be romantic and screamed at the same time. Screaming violates the essence of romance.*

Ten minutes later, the train arrived at the station in Paris. As Thomas exited the train station, attempting to take in the grandeur of Paris seemed analogous to examining fifty art paintings at once. The visual stimulation was spine-tingling. This was unquestionably a much larger city than Bordeaux, and it was the first time that he had stepped foot in a city of this size. He had never been to New York City or even Chicago in the United States; his parents hadn't had the economic means to do much traveling outside of Indiana. Nor did they have much interest in leaving the state, either. Thomas could see that life took place here in Paris on a completely different scale. There were gorgeous, gleaming boulevards. There were countless sidewalk cafés and he could even see the famous Notre Dame Cathedral in the distance. It was not hype that this was a deeply romantic city. He could feel the romance in the air. Even the oxygen that he breathed in seemed to have this romantic ethos. Everywhere that he walked and looked around, this feeling encapsulated him.

He stayed in a youth hostel that night, which was another completely novel experience. Thomas had never slept in a room with multiple beds before. Although it felt like a gross invasion of privacy (it felt a bit like the famous novel *1984* in which Big Brother was watching his every move), it also offered social opportunities to meet other travelers. It would be difficult to meet this many other people in a hotel. *Not unless I attempted to crash through their window into the room and speak to them. But I doubt that this approach would turn out well.*

Thomas saw several travelers in his room with very large

backpacks. *I hope that there are no dead bodies in these backpacks. It might be difficult to sleep tonight if I am woken up by the stench of rotting flesh. Perhaps they are just doing a lot of traveling.* He greeted an athletic-looking, blond male.

"How's it going?"

"Doing great. How about yourself, mate?"

"I'm exhausted after my train ride. Where are you from?"

"From Australia. There's a group of four of us doing an extended trip through Europe. We spent a week in the U.K. and now we're checking out France. This hostel is quite nice actually; we stayed in another one for the last couple days that was a bit on the dodgy side."

Thomas had never met anyone from Australia before. He mostly understood what the guy was saying, but he was not used to his accent and how he pronounced his words. He had never heard anyone address him as "mate" before, although he seemed to remember this term from the movie *Crocodile Dundee.* He liked it though. It gave a friendly touch to the conversation. He had previously met a couple of guys from California who used the term "dude" instead, but that had not felt as friendly. To Thomas, the frequent use of the term "dude" communicated an image of the person being stoned rather than being friendly. Thomas had never heard the term "dodgy" used before, but he was able to figure out the meaning from the context.

"I assume that you are American?" the Aussie asked.

"Indeed. I'm finishing up a short work experience here in France, and I need to figure out where I am going to travel next. My host family said that I should come to Paris for a few days and search in an international bookstore for ideas about my next travel destination. My name is Thomas, by the way."

"I'm Ron. I think that I've seen a quite large bookstore with an English section here, mate. How about tomorrow evening we can grab some dinner and then afterwards we'll head over to that bookstore? I might find some useful information there as well, and I think that some of my other mates could be interested too."

"That sounds great."

Thomas was quite impressed by Ron's friendliness. He was not accustomed to someone almost immediately offering to be so helpful and asking him if he wanted to join him and his friends for dinner. *Perhaps these Australians are more open and friendly than what I am used to. It was much harder to develop my friendships back home. I thought that possibly he would offer suggestions, but I did not expect Ron to invite me to dinner and offer to accompany me to the bookstore with no hesitation. Who knew that making connections in a youth hostel was this easy? I merely thought that this would be a cheap place to crash for the night on my bellhop wages, but I am also making some social connections now with people from the other side of the world.*

It seems to be the case with travel that not only obviously do I meet the natives in that country, but I also meet lots of other travelers from other countries. So, in addition to learning about the native culture, I gain opportunities to learn about the cultures of the other travelers. It is almost like two for the price of one. From one experience, I am able to learn about many cultures. It is also possible that I could meet foreigners in some areas of the United States, but it is not the same type of experience for me to meet them on my home turf. When I am at home, in my comfort zone, my thought processes and orientation are different. Additionally, in this case, I would be talking to them as a native. However, when we are both foreigners in the country, then we immediately share that in common. We also are both outside of our comfort zones; this causes our interactions to be different. Also, I am more likely to meet foreigners when traveling. When I am traveling,

I participate in specific experiences that guarantee that I will meet other foreigners.

Thomas felt that this seemed to be the case of the rich getting richer. While he was already immersed in one culture, the experience in and of itself made it more likely that he would be exposed to other cultures as well. Additionally, these experiences made him want to continue traveling and keep deepening the well. Likewise, wealthy individuals already have significantly more savings than the rest of humankind. With these savings, they are able to invest their money and then get richer through dividends, capital gains, etc. These gains, in turn, encourage them to keep investing and growing their wealth. Meanwhile, the person back home who had never traveled did not realize that he was missing out on all these experiences. He continues to live his normal, customary life and continues to miss out on these deep exposures that broaden his mind and shake up his cultural foundations. *Yes,* Thomas thought, *trends tend to perpetuate themselves. It seems to be one of the laws of human experience. This is one of the great challenges to the justice of human existence: the skewed playing field.*

The next day, Thomas met the other three "mates", or friends of Ron. One of the other Aussies, David, had the appearance of an artist. His hair was quite long, with a ponytail. His ears were pierced, and he had a deep beard. The other two guys, Damian and Craig, had less unusual appearances. They all had the enormous backpacks, and they all seemed to have a very relaxed demeanor. For them, the conversation seemed to be quite joyous, while Thomas felt a much greater sense of anxiety. He found himself crossing his arms and twiddling with the straw in his drink as a nervous reaction. *Inside, my circulatory system is analogous to a hospital waiting room, while theirs is similar to a meditation class,* he thought.

"Alright, mate, are you ready to head out for the bookstore and some dinner?" Damian asked.

"I am," Thomas replied.

"We'll have dinner near Galignani. It's the oldest English-language bookstore in Europe. This should meet your needs. If it fails, we'll find another one. It's a thirty-minute subway ride from here, so you'll get some nice views of the birds on the subway."

"I don't understand. There are birds on the subway?"

"Right, mate, I was working in the U.K. before I met up with my mates to travel around Europe. That's one term for girls over there. Paris is a style capital, so these views on the subway are well worth the price of your train ticket. A trip to Paris is a great investment for that reason alone," Damian said with a sharp grin, fully showing his somewhat yellow-looking teeth.

"Now you are going to really confuse me, incorporating both British and Australian English into your speech. I won't know which terms are associated with which country."

"No worries, mate. If I bring up any more British-isms, I'll try to point that out. That's assuming it's before drinking. We Aussies can really put it away when it comes to the booze."

"Do you ever worry about damage to your liver from too much drinking?" Thomas asked.

"You're cracking me up, mate. You're clearly not an Aussie. I have had so many great nights out. After all of the fun that I have had, you think that I'm worried about my liver? If I could speak to my liver, I'd say, 'Sorry for the pain, mate, but I couldn't resist all of the brilliant nights and chasing tail.' You only live once, mate. Better to die earlier and have enjoyed your life than to live a long life and be miserable."

"I see your point, but I suppose that I don't enjoy drinking that much. I find greater fulfillment from a quiet evening of reading and contemplation. And this is much healthier for my liver," Thomas noted. "I can't spend a quiet evening with a book and not feel bored out of my mind. As I said, I'd much rather party hard and die earlier if that's the consequence. Before you leave Paris, we're going to have one fun evening with you. We'll show you the Aussie way, mate. If you stumble back into this room sloshed, then we've accomplished our mission here."

"Anyways, Damian, don't put too much pressure on the Yank. We'll show him this bookstore first before we make any attempt to get him wasted on the streets of Paris," Ron said.

Clearly, Thomas had met another partier; these were the same types of people that he despised so much in the United States. However, for some reason, he did not feel the same antipathy towards Damian. *He is definitely a partier, but he still has a larger interest in the human world*, Thomas thought. *After all, he is very far from his native country and he also spent time in the U.K. In his case, he seems to combine an interest in travel and culture with partying. This must be why it does not feel as repulsive to me.* His college classmates who were partiers were completely insular. They were exclusively focused on hard drinking and socializing. However, the same case could not plausibly be argued about Damian. He had still taken a grand step into the unknown by backpacking through Europe with his buddies. *In many respects, he combines both my character and the character of my foes at home. If he is able to really enjoy himself in crowds of people, this is not necessarily a detrimental aspect of character. Yes, harshly judging all extroverts was quite irrational. Can I argue that I am more of a "real" traveler than him? Not really. We are both in the same situation here in Paris, and we both are attempting to absorb this gorgeous city.*

The Galignani bookstore was several metro stops away at the Jardin des Tuileries stop. They walked over to the metro. It was early evening, and Thomas was indeed struck by the beauty of many of the women that he saw on the streets and when they were on the metro. He first noticed that Parisian women did not wear ordinary clothes; they did not wear plain-looking jeans and t-shirts that were common back in Indiana. Their dress was extremely stylish. High heels were omnipresent. Many of them dressed in black. Many of the color combinations were quite subtle as well. *These women spend a lot of time shopping for their wardrobes and putting them together,* he thought. *These outfits are not just slopped together in a few minutes in the morning. No wonder these Aussie dudes think that the train ride to Paris is worth it merely for the eye candy!*

I better not tell Paul that the women are more attractive in Paris! If I say that anything is superior in Paris compared to Bordeaux, I might be homeless when I get back. Either that or he'll tell me that I was looking at Parisian women after I drank too much inferior Parisian wine, which distorted my vision. He'll say that the wine glaucoma gave me my delusional taste for Parisian women. He could already hear Paul telling him that he was a typical American tourist; he was too easily impressed by the grandiosity of Paris and he hadn't taken enough care and diligence to appreciate the subtleties of Bordeaux, blah, blah, blah. *I like Bordeaux as well; I don't think that I was ever particularly negative about it. It just seems a bit pedantic to be resistant to any opinion that suggests that something in Paris might be better than something in Bordeaux.*

Thomas heard a lot of French conversations occurring on the subway. He realized that although he had learned a lot of French in his lessons, he could only understand about fifteen percent of the conversations that he was hearing. He rarely could understand a full sentence; he mostly just understood words here and there. He did hear "merci" which was one of the more basic French words that a beginning speaker would know (thank you). They were speaking much too fast for him to process it. He realized that this was a big difference between a person's native language and a foreign language that a person didn't speak very well. With the native tongue, he could hear the words and not have to think very much. But with French, it required much more processing and thinking. He had to try and understand the pronunciation, try and remember what the names of the words were, and put them all together into a sentence at a very fast pace while the person was speaking. Often, he was still processing what he was hearing, but the speaker had moved on to four or five other sentences. *We Americans are quite favored that we are not forced to learn another language. It is negative from an intellectual development standpoint, but it is quite difficult and can be a real hassle. I feel exhausted just trying to understand these conversations on the subway. Imagine how foreigners in the U.S. must feel who are forced to learn English for their jobs or because they want to study at a better university.*

Thomas saw that to be a traveler meant putting himself in someone else's clothes. No matter what he did, this theme kept striking him on the head over and over again. On the subway, he was in the wardrobe of a foreign speaker trying to understand the conversations of people around him. Walking the streets with his Aussie acquaintances, he was in the shoes of someone who was not familiar with the cultural mores of his surroundings. He had felt the experience of discrimination for the first time when the man screamed at him in the hotel as an "evil foreigner", and that experience repeated itself on the train when the man next to him was furious that he could not speak French well. Feeling stereotyped as an American was an uncommon experience as well compared to his previous life. Again, he realized that he had to be able to endure a lot of discomfort while traveling in order to be able to fully benefit from the experience. *I cannot take two steps forward unless I experience the pain and inconvenience of one step backward. Growth never comes effortlessly. Life simply does not work that way. I probably will not even realize how much I have changed until I am actually back in Indiana. Now, I am in the traveling zone, struggling to adapt to changing, unfamiliar conditions. The adjustments and difficulties are at the center of my focus most of the time. Whenever I do return to my comfort zone in Indiana, I will be able to reflect more fully on all of these challenges and growth opportunities.*

As he looked around on the subway, he saw that a lot of people were reading a newspaper called *Le Monde*. He knew from his French lessons that this translated as "The World", which certainly seemed like a logical title for a newspaper. He knew enough French to have some conversation. He really wanted to ask someone what they thought of the newspaper. *Yes, I am taking a risk approaching a stranger on the subway in Paris. But I would rather know that I tried to find out about* Le Monde *than wonder what would have occurred if I had asked.*

Near him was a very beautiful French woman in her late twenties or early thirties. Seated next to her was an old French man in a gray suit. Both of them happened to be reading *Le Monde*. *I might as well try talking to the woman.* He said in French: "Sorry to bother you, Madame, but I am only visiting Paris. What is your opinion of *Le Monde* as a newspaper?"

"Are you American?" she replied in French.

"Yes," he said.

She then switched over to English. "I speak some English. I appreciate that you tried to speak to me in French. You are ahead of most of the other Americans that I have talked to here. Impressive that you can speak some sentences of another language," she said with a stoic countenance.

Thomas felt slightly embarrassed, but he did not say anything. *She does have a point. It is rather blunt to put it that way, but generally, Americans are not very multilingual.*

"*Le Monde* does not report about Britney Spears or Kardashians. This is deep discussion for our issues and world issues. I suggest that you try to read it when you are in Paris," she said, still maintaining an expressionless countenance.

This woman may be gorgeous, but she has about as much charm as a porcupine. Looks are certainly not the whole shebang. I would probably rather cuddle with a porcupine. I don't think that the quills would be as painful as how this lady speaks to me. I almost feel like words have a greater ability to wound people than punches sometimes. The effects of words can linger longer, although if I were severely beaten into a coma, then that would be a more distinctive situation. Even though he acknowledged that the woman had a point about Americans, he still felt that his pride had been wounded from the exchange. He had spoken just a few words of French and she was impressed by that? Again, he felt highly stereotyped as an ignorant American. *The problem is when we as individuals deviate from statistical tendencies of our nationality, race, and so on. The statistical generalization may have some validity, but it does not mean that I conform to it as an individual. And I want to be judged as an individual, not lumped in with others who do not share my behavior.*

I wish that she could have just thanked me for speaking to her in French, but they do seem to have a lot of resentment against us

Americans. I should tell her that I am going to follow her suggestion and read Le Monde. *If she starts to have more positive experiences with Americans, then at least there is some possibility that she could change her perception. Furthermore, I should not get defensive about Americans. That will just add more fuel to the French fire that we Americans are too proud of ourselves.*

"Thank you for the suggestion. I am definitely going to spend some time reading *Le Monde.* I came to France because I wanted to see another culture and begin to absorb the ways of the rest of the world. I believe that being exposed to the opinions of a well-respected French newspaper would help me along this path," he replied calmly.

His response seemed to break her stolid countenance. She was quite surprised that he reacted so diplomatically to her comment and even grinned slightly, at a Paul-like grin level.

"You will not be sad that you tried to read *Le Monde.* It is la crème de la crème of newspapers," she said, winking at him, which heavily exposed her quite noticeable eyeliner.

Maybe I would slightly rank her company ahead of a porcupine. It is not likely that a porcupine would have enlightened me about Le Monde. *She did come across as a bit gruff and cantankerous at first, but she was willing to speak to me. The old man on the train completely gave me the cold shoulder. Sometimes, as an American, I need to be grateful for even very small, basic interactions here. I can only hope that this woman will meet a few more Americans who will help her shatter her stereotype.*

Reading a high-quality newspaper seems to be a decent method of gaining insights into another culture. Some newspapers claim to be "objective", but is any human being truly objective? How can we prevent our biases and assumptions from influencing our work? It seems almost impossible, akin to a far-fetched dream. Even in a purportedly factual newspaper in France, I would probably be able to discern some cultural differences. However, I do not need to concern myself with this nearly as much with <u>Le Monde</u> *because those writers are opinionated anyway. Yes, I believe that this woman is quite correct that exposure to these opinions of the French intelligentsia would be quite worthwhile. I've certainly heard a lot of ideas from Paul over his infallible Bordeaux wine, but some diversity would be useful.*

Thomas also realized from this conversation some of the virtues of public transport. Up to this point, his experience with public transportation had been virtually nonexistent. In Indiana, just about everyone traveled by car; there was certainly no subway to speak of. Although there was far less privacy on the subway, it did open up greater avenues for social interaction; it was analogous to comparing a youth hostel with a hotel. *Would I have been exposed to* <u>Le Monde</u>*? Would I have had this interesting (though slightly off-putting) conversation with that gorgeous French woman?* Thomas doubted it.

Riding on the subway also allowed for an opportunity to people watch. *It is probably safe to assume that just about everyone in Paris uses the subway. Therefore, I am most likely seeing a very representative cross section of Parisian society. Is there any other type of experience in Paris that shows me as much of a cross section? True, I can walk around certain neighborhoods. But neighborhoods usually have distinctive characteristics and are not nearly as cross-sectional. A neighborhood might be particularly wealthy or poor, or it could be dominated by the Arab sub-population of Paris. The subway seems like much more of a great equalizer, especially in Europe where public transportation seems to be much more a part of the culture. Possibly, some wealthy individuals in Paris never use the subway. But it does seem to draw a diverse population, and a lot of the people in these subway cars certainly do not "look" poor. Parking seems to be fairly limited in Paris and there is quite a bit of traffic, so it is quite conceivable that many well-off individuals would prefer the convenience of the subway.* He almost wished that he was spending more time in Paris. *What else could I learn from multiple subway rides in this grand capital? The Aussies emphasize the eye candy of the Parisian women, but if I look beyond that, there are so many other possibilities. Learning about* Le Monde *seems to be just the tip of the iceberg.*

All of the senses are stimulated much more on public transit. I can possibly smell foods, overhear conversations, and observe fashions and behaviors. The car certainly seems to mesh well with the American self-centered ethos. The car is meant to cater to my individual needs. Subways and other forms of public transit are much more communal and require more compromises about destinations.

Possibly, that is one reason why public transit is so much less developed in the Midwestern part of the United States. It simply does not mesh with the lifestyle and the orientation of the population. He also knew from his time in France that it was much more expensive to drive in France and Europe generally. The cost of gas was much higher. Therefore, most likely, many people used public transit out of economic necessity as well. *It seems to be a gross oversimplification to attribute the much higher use of public transit here simply to a stronger community-oriented style of living. The economic factors were probably just as powerful, if not more so.*

They were now almost at the metro stop for the bookstore. The Aussies had been chatting with each other the entire time while he was lost in his own thoughts. Once again, he felt extremely introverted compared to them. The subway ride seemed to show a classic difference between introverts and extroverts. Introverts tend to be much more stimulated by what is *inside* themselves (mainly their own mind and experiences such as reading that stimulate the mind). Extroverts are much more stimulated by *outside* events. They thrive on socializing. The Aussies were most likely enjoying their conversations every bit as much as Thomas had enjoyed being trapped inside his own head. He also realized that society needed both kinds of people. If everyone were extroverted or introverted, then much would be lost. If there were only extroverts, there would be few writers, scientists, mathematicians, etc. If everyone were introverted though, business leadership and political leadership would likely suffer, among other things. If only one of the two types existed, this seemed akin to half of a coin. *A coin, by its very essence, must have a head and a tail. Take away one, and it is no longer a coin.*

They exited the subway and walked towards the bookstore. As Thomas traversed the first crosswalk, a car nearly hit him, pulling up behind him to turn onto the street. *Obviously, Paul is not the only insane driver in this country,* he thought. It was an interesting question regarding why the drivers seem worse here compared to Indiana. He had felt a lower level of respect generally from people here compared to at home. Did this lower level of respect cause the psychotic driving? Was it related to impulse control? The French were known as legendary romantics. Arguably, a key factor relating to being very romantic was acting strongly on impulses. If these impulses were present behind the steering wheel as well, then this could have some explanatory power. *What is the correlation between passionate romantics and brusque driving? Clearly, these impulses could be used for both beneficial purposes (love) and very detrimental ones (reckless driving).*

As his shock from near contact with a car subsided, they entered the bookstore. He was pleased; the place was ample enough for a game of hide-and-seek. *The Aussies made a good choice, coming here. There is a notable selection of books. I've never seen so many travel books before. Are there enough travel books here to cover the distance between Paris and Bordeaux?*

Ron showed him where the travel section was located. He knew that the United States had large bookstores as well; he had just never experienced them. He first browsed through *Lonely Planet India*. He had studied some aspects of Indian culture in a college religion class, and he knew that it would be a deeply exotic experience if he decided to pursue an opportunity there. He knew that they were quite spiritual, based on his knowledge of Hinduism and the demographics of the country. But the book that he was glancing through mentioned that there was a lot of very visible poverty there, and that the sanitary conditions were often significantly worse than what many Western people were accustomed to. *I'm not quite sure if I am ready for that big of a cultural adjustment. I have only had one foreign travel experience so far in a pretty wealthy country. I believe that this might be too grand a reach. I have struggled enough with adapting to France; what if this experience would put me over the edge psychologically? To embark upon an experience in which I feel completely astounded on a daily basis would defeat the spirit of a foreign travel experience.*

These thoughts reminded Thomas of the phrase "don't throw out the baby with the bathwater". *I would like an experience where I am continually stimulated, learning, and expanding my awareness, but I also must maintain my mental balance and some semblance of sanity. It is not a simple endeavor to find the right balance of sanity and stimulation in a foreign travel experience. But it seems like an unwise decision to take a gamble on a place where I worry that I would be easily overwhelmed. No, India sounds like more of a place for very seasoned travelers. I am not at that level after one brief experience. For me, travel immersion is a step-by-step process. Most life experiences follow this general principle. We learn concepts and improve ourselves in bits and pieces. Most of the time, I feel that a mile of effort is required for an inch of any kind of growth. I often had to study for hours for an exam that lasted for one hour. Often, when I am reading a difficult book, intense concentration is required for an hour to read merely ten pages. Yes, we must struggle for every inch of progress.*

Growing through foreign travel is no different. The laws and statistical tendencies of human experience do not abruptly change merely because I am in a foreign land. I still experience the ebbs and flows of human emotion.

Just as chemicals reach equilibrium during reactions and forces in physics have counter-reactions, at the human level, there must be some kind of psychological equivalent of homeostasis. Does this contradict my hunch that I would self-destruct in India? No. For the natives, there is some kind of homeostasis there because they are accustomed to those conditions. A society that completely lacks homeostasis would degenerate into Thomas Hobbes's state of nature. Possibly Afghanistan or the most violent African countries are good examples of this failure to attain any kind of reasonable homeostasis. But from what I know about India, they have not collapsed into a state of nature; it just sounds like the conditions are quite different from my comfort level. As a foreigner there, I might possibly lose my mental balance, but the natives are able to maintain some kind of steady equilibrium. At least I hope so for their sake. This is a grueling enough existence with homeostasis. Imagine the mental angst if I were living in a violent state of nature? I do not know how people in those conditions are able to persevere. They must have coping skills that I lack.

As Thomas continued to browse the travel section, another

country that caught his eye was China. *They are an emerging power. That could be quite useful to experience a society that will have a lot of future importance.* Ron was fairly close by in another section. Thomas wondered if any of the Aussies had words of advice about pursuing an opportunity in China.

"Ron, can I ask you a question?"

"Of course, mate. What can I do for you?"

"Have you ever been to China?"

"Unfortunately, not yet. But I have a mate who taught English there for a couple of years."

Ron's friend had taught English overseas. Thomas's eyes widened upon hearing this. He had not thought of that option yet. *There are probably lots of opportunities to do that in different places. That could be a very stimulating way to immerse myself in the culture if I speak to students. That might be a less arduous means of cultural interaction compared to approaching stunning women on the subway or jousting with scowling old men next to me on the train.*

"What did your mate say about the experience?"

"He said that he learned a lot, but he went through a large amount of culture shock during the first year. He found many aspects of the culture to be hard to deal with. He had done a lot of traveling, so he thought that he could handle China. But it was far more exotic than most of the other places that he had been."

"Did he mention which aspects of his experience that he found to be the most difficult?"

"I didn't have a lot of detailed conversations about it, mate, but I do remember that he said that the cleanliness of many places such as restaurants and bathrooms was lacking. He said that it took him a long time to get used to people pushing and shoving through lines, and he also said that a lot of people spoke at very loud volumes, so he struggled to get peace and quiet very often. He said that he was constantly bombarded by noise, loud conversations, rowdy behavior, and other such things. I can put him in touch with you if you would like to chat about these issues more."

"Thank you for the offer, Ron, but it sounds to me like China might not be the ideal next destination for me. I'm looking for a thought-provoking foreign experience, but without a disproportionate amount of culture shock. I still consider myself to be somewhat of a novice foreign traveler. I'm trying to ease my way into these unfamiliar foreign environments. Just a few months ago, I was a college kid in rural Indiana who had hardly ever left his own state! You could say that I'm a bit more of a British gradualist than a Russian revolutionary when it comes to jumping into foreign oceans," Thomas concluded with a smirk.

Ron laughed, almost bumping into another lady who was passing by. "Well, if you're too much of a Russian revolutionary, mate, your next foreign experience could be your last one. You might become an expert on prisons in different countries though."

"I'm not seeking that kind of transcontinental knowledge."

"Ha, well, I don't blame you, mate. Not all exotic knowledge is worth getting. I won't debate you on that one."

"Do you have any suggestions for possible next destinations for me based on what I have just told you?"

"Are you definitely looking to go to an Asian destination?"

"I wouldn't say that it's an absolute must, but I think that it would be a good choice. Obviously, I have gained a very European experience by spending time in France. I certainly think that it would broaden my mindset to be immersed in an Asian culture."

"That's a fair point, mate. You might want to consider Japan.

You'll still get a very different experience, but it's a well-off country economically, so that aspect won't overwhelm you. It's also very clean, so that will help ease the adjustment factor as well. But without a doubt, you will gain exposure to a unique way of thinking. Japan is extremely different from anywhere else that I've ever been, mate. If you go there, you'll have to chuck away many of your Western assumptions if you want to have a pleasant experience."

When Thomas heard this suggestion, he was on cloud nine. He had even considered Japan as a possible first destination for his travel adventures. He had originally considered Japan since he was familiar with many Japanese companies from consumer electronics. Japan also appealed to him because of his deep interest in history. He wondered what they would say about the Atom bomb. *It has been fascinating to see historical cathedrals in France. If I were able to visit Nagasaki and Hiroshima, that would really be an eye-opening connection to tangible history and the devastation of war. Sure, I learned a lot of history in classes back in school. I spent many hours reading my textbooks and discussing different points of view in my classes. But actually viewing these historical sites is a completely different historical lens. It has made me realize that this history is real. It was not fiction that was created in someone's mind and then written into a book. It was part of physical reality and it has affected these nations as they have developed and formed their characters. If I have found it so visually powerful to see cathedrals and old streets, imagine expanding my historical appreciation by seeing Nagasaki or sites connected with geishas or the old Shogun order?*

He realized that the West is just a fraction of humanity's experience. *It will give me a much more holistic view to spend my next travel sojourn in Asia. There are always questions of depth vs. breadth. Some people might be more inclined to keep exploring Europe in order to get a more nuanced view of the continent. There is certainly merit in having depth of knowledge.*

But my gut tells me that I am more inclined towards breadth. Since our existence on this planet is relatively short, I would rather know that I gained breadth of knowledge. I would like to have a more complete understanding of the whole. That is ultimately more satisfying than merely having a more nuanced view of Europe. Besides, I can always return to Europe later. Nothing prevents me from eventually exploring this continent in greater depth. But I will also see Europe with new eyes after I have spent time in Japan. Exposure to Eastern culture will give me yet another lens through which to process my perceptions and reactions here. If I go to my grave having seen nothing more than France on this continent, then I will without a doubt be full of regrets. But I will have even greater regrets if I go to the grave having never explored outside of the West. With limited time and often limited financial resources, I have to make difficult choices all the time. Every time I make a choice, I give up something. So then, the question is not am I giving up something, but given my choices, what is the greater good and what is the greater setback? From this paradigm, it is significantly worse to perish without having experienced cultures outside of the West.

It would be analogous to never having used my lower body. If my lower body were completely paralyzed, it would indeed be unfortunate, and it would sharply limit my movements. Likewise, if I were intellectually paralyzed from never stepping outside of the West, it would sharply limit my potential for understanding and awareness. It would confine me too much inside a metaphorical box if I only am familiar with the mores and traditions of the West.

Teaching English sounds like an attractive option. Surely, that would be more interesting than working at a hotel? Thomas began browsing one of the Japan books, searching for the section on working abroad. The book did have a lot of useful information. He was clearly eligible for teaching positions as a native English speaker. The book also said that a bachelor's degree was usually required to obtain most teaching positions in Japan; this would not be any obstacle for him either. The book noted that for positions at smaller language schools, he would need to go to Japan first and interview there. However, there were a few larger "chain" schools that interviewed in Western cities. It mentioned London as one common interview destination; that meant that he might not have to return to the United States before his next foreign experience. The book also indicated that taking a TEFL (Teaching English as a Foreign Language) certification course would be helpful, but it was not required to obtain a teaching position in Japan. *I think that I would like to see if I enjoy teaching in general and living in Japan in particular before I invest any money in certification courses. I should ask Ron about that.* He moved over to the science section on the other side of the floor, where Ron was browsing through a book.

"Ron, did your friend who taught in China have any kind of certification?"

Ron looked up, smiled, and closed the book. "I don't think so, mate. He said that his teaching job was basically like being a talking monkey, and that he didn't really need the certification. He did say that if you want to get better jobs teaching at a university with some nicer perks, then those certifications can be worth it. But if you just want to mess around in Japan for a year or so, I don't think that you should worry yourself sick about certifications, mate. Do you think that you can meet expectations as a talking monkey?"

"Indeed I do. I don't have to teach inside a cage though, do I?"

"Not literally is what I understand. My mate in China did talk about feeling caged in in terms of lacking any rights as an employee or worker, but I don't think that he was actually in a cage," Ron said with a large chuckle.

"Well, if I were teaching in China caged up, I would put on a panda costume some days for variety. Then I would ask my students if it were easier to learn English from a talking monkey or a talking panda, and then I would ask them to justify their answers! They would probably understand my humor about as well as my French host family did," Thomas said.

"Well, from what I understand, the Chinese are pretty blunt. They will definitely give you a straightforward answer regarding which animal is a better teacher. Maybe they will tell you that it's less intimidating speaking a weird language to a panda. Or perhaps they will tell you that a white dude has no business dressing up like one of their animals," Ron said, laughing heartily.

"Yeah, I can't speak for the Chinese or for pandas. Though American culture might be closer to pandas."

"I'm not quite sure about that comparison, mate. You Americans have a pretty war-like history. Cuddly pandas aren't what I, as an Australian, think of too much when I start thinking about American culture."

"You have a fair point, Ron. Anyways, returning to reality, this book says that I can interview for positions with the larger language schools in some Western cities. They do interviews in London. I think that I will go there."

"That sounds like a great plan, mate. I think that you're making a great decision to teach in Japan. It will give you a lifetime of memories that you can talk about."

Thomas strongly agreed with Ron. His gut feeling was that

the decision was right. *Going to Japan will be a good balance of novelty and comfort based on what I know. I will get exposed to a different culture, but it sounds unlikely that I will be completely overpowered by the adjustment. I am fortunate that I met these Aussie guys in the youth hostel. Who knows if I would have made the same decision if I had not met them? It was just chance that we happened to meet in that youth hostel. So many outcomes in life seem to rest on chance. Finding a romantic soul mate certainly had a strong chance component, as did searching for jobs and many other endeavors. But this does add a bit of flavor to life. If our existence were completely deterministic and law-like, that would be too constricting. I would not want to live if those were life's conditions.*

"I think that I have accomplished my mission at the bookstore. How much longer do you and your buddies want to stay here?"

"I'll check up on them, mate. I would imagine that we can leave pretty soon."

They left shortly afterwards. They ate at a "fast casual" place for dinner. Damian and Craig said that they did not want to spend hours eating at a traditional French restaurant. "I've enjoyed some of the food that I've had in France, but eating at some of these restaurants kills my whole evening. It doesn't allow enough time for going to the bar!" Damian said.

"You can imbibe on good quality wine at a nice French restaurant," Thomas responded.

"Well, that gets very expensive, mate. Drinking beer is more economical and that tends to be more the Aussie way of a night out, though we do drink wine on occasion. It's not a part of our culture, though, to the extent that it is in France," he replied.

"Sure, the same would be true of the United States as well."

Thomas contented himself with a simple ham and cheese sandwich (a croque monsieur) with fries; he remembered that they were called "freedom fries" during the Iraq war. *There does not seem to be anything particularly French about fries anyway. They remind me more of Southern cuisine than French food since, in the South, they love to fry everything. No wonder so many people are so religious in the South. Some of them are going to need divine intervention to live long on those deep-fried diets that are soaked in butter.* The croque monsieur, though, was definitely distinguishable from a standard American ham and cheese sandwich. The seasoning was different, and the cheese was on top of the bread rather than inside the sandwich. If someone were to ask him if his meal completely lacked "Frenchness", he would definitely shake his head in response.

They followed up their meal by heading over to the bar, which is when the evening officially started for Damian and Craig. Ron and David also drank at least four or five beers, but this was light drinking compared to their friends. Damian easily downed eight beers in a few hours. Thomas remembered that he said before that he loves to drink. He was definitely a man of his word. Thomas drank one beer very slowly to be sociable. The Aussies asked him several times if he wanted another drink, but he declined each time. *These guys have too much of a drinking culture for my tastes. Heavy drinking is just not part of my nature, plain and simple. At least I've never had to clean the bathroom from vomiting.*

I wonder if vomit is as common as water in Damian's bathroom. He may have developed a high tolerance from so much "experience" though; that means that he isn't necessarily vomiting all the time. Thomas did remember many of his college classmates ruining the dormitory bathrooms with nauseous episodes, but he considered that it's certainly possible that Damian was more of a "professional". *That's right: a "professional" drinker. Possibly, he*

88

is a person who is capable of holding his liquor and he does it with some class. Maybe it's a virtue that I was exposed to such yahoos at my high school and college. It makes me appreciate that these Aussie dudes are more refined drinkers in comparison. There is a tendency to think that no good can come out of human suffering or bad experiences, but this seems to miss the mark. Bad experiences help us appreciate something better, or at least they should. Suffering can aid us in giving perspective and proportionality to our lives. If life were exclusively filled with pleasure, it is difficult to understand how all of the pleasure could retain its meaning. There must be a mix of pleasure and pain. Otherwise, the human homeostasis that I was pondering earlier could not be obtained.

Damian and Craig were not inhibited about chatting with the ladies in the bar. Thomas did concede that this was an advantage of social drinking; "normal" inhibitions were swept under the rug when under the influence. A bit later in the evening, they beckoned to Ron and Thomas to come over to their beer-laced consultation.

They were talking to a group of four women, and Thomas was able to engage in a one-on-one conversation with one of them. He was pleasantly surprised that the conversation was being conducted in English. He was excited to be able to converse with some more French women, but this woman looked a bit different than the French ladies whom he had seen in the street. She was absolutely drop-dead gorgeous, with dark hair and olive skin. He had already forgotten her non-French-sounding name. She was significantly more tan than most of the French ladies in the surroundings.

"Your accent doesn't sound French. Do you mind if I ask where you are from?" Thomas asked.

"It would be big surprise if my accent is French," she replied with a laugh. "Do you have a guess?"

"I haven't been to many countries, so it is challenging to guess. Are you from somewhere else in Europe?"

"No, I am from Israel," she said, making strong eye contact.

He wondered in the back of his mind if she was possibly flirting with him. *She comes across as more warm than most of the Parisians.*

"What brought you to Paris?"

"I am finish last term at Paris Descartes University."

"Do you study in French?"

"Yes. My parents are from France and later immigrated to Israel. I am native level at French. What do you do here?"

"I am participating in a work program in hospitality in Bordeaux. I came up to Paris to see the capital. It is my first time outside of the United States."

"How you find it...American in France?"

"I definitely feel stereotyped a lot, but the experience has been fascinating. I wouldn't trade it for the best car on the planet," he said with a mischievous look.

"Every country has their version of America stereotype. How can we not from TV and movies? Israel has complex relationship with America. We can discuss it in detail next time."

Good sign! She seems to want to meet again.

"Why did your parents immigrate to Israel?"

"They want to explore their Jewish identity more. France has some advantage, but they wanted to live in Jewish nation. Israel is much more Mediterranean lifestyle. In Tel Aviv, we are right on beach. It is amazing city, you should visit."

This conversation filled Thomas with joyful energy. He found himself salivating over her charming, ultra-feminine voice, in addition to her incredibly attractive appearance. A mere hour ago, he was dead set on traveling to Japan. Now, his libido was complicating his plans.

"I haven't made a final decision about where I will travel next. Israel does sound intriguing though."

"You are sincere man. I can tell. We like honest, straightforward people in our culture. Let's stay in touch."

"Please remind me of your name again."

"Sendi."

"Okay, that sounds a bit like 'Cindy'. This association will help me to remember."

He took down Sendi's email and phone number, and then she left the bar with one of her friends. Thomas re-joined the larger conversation.

When Damian (and to a lesser extent Craig) had decided that they were satisfied that their livers had been damaged enough by the evening's activities, they left the bar. Damian was stumbling along and decided that he would be better off catching a taxi home. Craig joined him in the taxi as well. David and Ron accompanied Thomas back to the subway. According to them, their evening of four or five beers was "light drinking" for Aussie males.

Thomas did feel somewhat self-conscious about his low tolerance for alcohol compared to the Aussie guys, but he had noticed that his skin had thickened quite a bit from the experience of being a foreigner in France. In college, he had felt completely alienated; now, he merely just felt self-conscious to some lesser degree. *Being in this uncomfortable position abroad has done wonders for my coping skills. It seems to be a much smaller matter if I stick out a bit from my company now after what I've been through in France. The experience where I was scorned in the restaurant for ordering apple juice and the time where the man seriously berated me in the hotel makes the experience with the Aussies extremely trivial in comparison. So much of our existence is defined by this tendency. Everything seems so relative to everything else. Are there any absolutes?*

A couple of days later, Thomas took the train back to Bordeaux. Even his brief stopover in Paris had broadened his view of France. Now he had seen with his own eyes both the bustling capital and a smaller city that evoked more traditional French culture. Thomas did agree to some degree with Paul that, at a minimum, it was more difficult for wine to have the same meaning in such a large city as Paris compared to Bordeaux. In Paris, there was always so much happening that wine was merely one entity in a sea of thousands. In Bordeaux, however, the city "breathed" wine much more. Its residents were fiercely proud of these wines. It was the center of attention to a much larger degree in a quieter place. The lack of hustle and bustle did help showcase the intrinsic French culture more; Thomas was convinced of that upon his return.

Going to Paris has helped me understand Paul's viewpoint more. Again, before I was held back by my lack of context. Bordeaux was the only French city that I had experienced. Therefore, I could not place it in a more complex mosaic of French reference points. I could listen to Paul's viewpoints, but evaluating them was an entirely different matter. The Paris sojourn has provided some much-needed diversity to my French experience. Thomas also realized from this fact that tourists who limited themselves to the capitals of Europe were missing part of the larger picture. It was necessary to also see smaller cities and towns when visiting a country. There wasn't anything "evil" in only experiencing the capitals, and it was superior to completely avoiding European or foreign travel. However, it was not the ideal method of European exploration. It had some merit, but it was strongly constrained by its limits. *Yes, large capitals are certainly not the whole picture of human existence. I have no reason to feel disappointment that I spent most of my time in France here in Bordeaux. I was able to view the country at a more relaxed pace, and feel the rhythms and melodies of French life in a more traditional setting that is not as influenced by globalization. Each country needs to retain its identity to some degree. If globalization turns the entire planet into only a few cultures, then humanity will have indeed suffered an immense loss. Reversing the trends of globalization seems to be a remote prospect, but hopefully it can at least be contained. If my hypothetical great-grandchildren visit Bordeaux, I also want them to be able to have this kind of exotic experience. I strongly hope that this wine culture will still be here, and that these historical buildings will still be standing. If my great-grandchildren find a homogenized city that has lost all traces of French culture and if they find that the historical places have been replaced by gleaming new buildings or fast food restaurants, then that will be a tragedy of Shakespearean proportions.*

Thomas knew that his homestay was coming to an end. It was now crucial to decide if he would sustain his original plan of traveling to Japan next. Altering all of his plans merely because of a pleasant conversation with a girl seemed to be quite a gamble, at best. His heart had been thoroughly set on Japan in the bookstore. Gorgeous women did have a hypnotizing effect on calculations, but he felt that it was important to step back rationally and evaluate his decision objectively. In any event, Sendi wouldn't be in Israel for at least a month and he also had the option of an Israel stopover after Japan. He hadn't signed a binding agreement that required returning to Indiana after the next adventure.

Yes, he believed that the best turn on this road was to preserve the original plan. It was a flattering self-esteem boost to draw interest from such an attractive girl, but he believed that he was far too young to be making all life decisions based on this facet of human existence. He had embarked on this international odyssey to open his mental floodgates to world cultures, and it seemed to be wise to keep that as the primary focus, not the tentative amorous interests of the last hour. Thomas knew he would not forget Sendi completely, but it seemed to be the wisest course to put her on the backburner for now.

The next day, he researched interviews for teaching positions in Japan, and he learned that one large company, Gova, was conducting interviews in London next month. He had been accepted for an interview slot; it didn't seem to be particularly tough to land an interview as long as he could provide a passport from a native English-speaking country. His visa was about to expire soon in France, but he decided that he would travel around Europe for a couple of weeks before the interview. His experience in the youth hostel had been quite positive; this inspired him to do more traveling. Meeting the Aussie guys had definitely raised his spirits. *Imagine whom else I could meet if I continue staying in youth hostels? It is quite reassuring to meet others who are curious about the world. I might have felt like a "freak" back home, but meeting these people reassures me that there are plenty of others who share my curiosity and yearning for knowledge. I might not be as unique as I used to think I was, but sometimes I do appreciate having somewhat like-minded company.*

This would be one of his last dinners at his host family's home. He had not yet told them about his future plans. Before heading down to dinner, he spoke to Paul in the family room while Marie was still preparing the dinner.

"I have decided on my next travel destination. Can you guess it?" he said with a minor grin.

"Can you tell me which general area it is in?" Paul asked.

"Asia."

"Did you decide to travel Thailand? The women in that country have a very beautiful reputation."

"That's not the only factor that motivates my traveling, Paul. If that were my main criteria, wouldn't I have gone to Italy instead of France?"

Paul's countenance froze. "I will not say that the Italian woman is not beautiful. But I cannot say that I find them more beautiful than the women in France. Perhaps I have some bias since I speak the same language as the French ladies, which adds to romantic experience."

"You also cannot French kiss with the Italian ladies."

Paul still had not warmed up to his attempts at humor. "You are very focused on all terms that have French in them, whether they are truly French or not. First, it was French fries and French toast. Now you have added the French kiss. If you travel to Italy, ask the ladies there if they have had a French kiss."

"I think I might give one to a lady on the train and ask her if she has ever experienced that before," Thomas replied.

Paul smiled slightly. "I am curious if you reach your destination from this action."

"Anyways, no, I'm not going to Thailand. It's a richer country than that."

"Ah. You decided to go to Japan?"

"Yes, indeed."

"Well, you said before that you wanted something different. That will be very different from France."

Paul did not have much else to say about this subject. His knowledge of Asia seemed to be limited to making comments about Thai women. *Maybe he slept with a prostitute from there. It seems odd that he would have thought about Thai women so quickly after I mentioned Asia. Well, I won't make any references to this conversation at dinner tonight. I may try to be a smart aleck quite often, but I haven't lost all of my judgment yet either.*

This will be one of my last dinners here. There is no guarantee that I will enjoy the food as much in Japan, Thomas thought with a frown. His exposure to Japanese food had been quite limited in Indiana; he didn't know much about Japanese cuisine.

"Marie, I am sad that this is one of my last dinners here."

She smiled, and replied in French. Paul translated for her. "She thinks that you have gained some good knowledge of our food. She has prepared many different dishes during your stay here," Paul said with the largest smile that Thomas had ever seen on his face. *I suppose once in a blue moon (or salmon-colored moon), he does show some emotion. It really has to be yanked out of him though.*

Paul informed Marie that Thomas would be going to Japan for his next destination. Her eyes and mouth opened wide, but she said nothing more. *Japan does seem to be outside of their universe. They do seem like a worldly, knowledgeable family, but that does not mean that they want to travel everywhere. I do not feel that they are provincial at all; they just have a much smaller sense of wanderlust compared to me. It isn't all black or white. There can be middle ground between people who are extremely provincial and people who love journeying to the entire globe. This family is somewhere in that amorphous middle. I have learned quite a bit from talking to Paul regardless. It has been extremely fascinating to learn his viewpoints about many different issues that we have discussed. I never would have been exposed to these opinions if I had stayed in Indiana, or at least it would have been extremely unlikely.*

A week later, Thomas bid farewell to his host family. He was usually extremely stoical, but he did feel a tear or two in his eye as he went through the process of saying goodbye. He had never stayed with another family before; without question, it had been a unique experience. There were certainly boundaries that he had felt. He was not part of their family, nor their culture or nation. But the experience had opened up his eyes to a larger world. *The experience was eye-opening, but I am still able to close my eyes as well today! That is a relief. It would defeat the purpose of an eye-opening experience if my eyes stayed open permanently. All of the dust and other particles that entered my eyes would make it much more trying to absorb new experiences. For every yin, there is a yang. It is very important that the more that my eyes widen from these foreign ventures, the power to contract and close these same eyes must remain as a counter-force. Has anyone else ever had these thoughts? I will not be able to answer that question today. Never being able to experience another mind is quite limiting! Just for one day, I want to be able to peer into someone else's mind, and hopefully the mind of an interesting person. It is much more difficult to place myself on the spectrum of humanity when I am forbidden from accessing any other minds. At most, I can make educated conjectures about how I am similar or different from other humans based on their external speech and actions. But it is an extremely incomplete picture. It reminds me of my college philosophy class, discussing Plato. The prisoners were stuck in the cave. They could only see shadows on the wall, and therefore, they were very limited in what kind of knowledge they could obtain.*

4

Chapter Four

October 2015

Due to his limited budget, he decided that he could not travel extensively during the two weeks preceding his London interview. He had saved up some cash from his hotel work, but it was not sufficient to finance an extensive trip. Thomas mostly stayed on a beach on the Spanish island of Majorca. Although Thomas was disappointed that he would not be able to explore more of Europe during this time, he was comforted by the fact that his salary in Japan would be an improvement, if he were hired. After that, he would have more opportunities for travel, he hoped. After the stress of working and living in France, beach relaxation did have some benefits. It was a nice contrast to be able to clear his mind and spend a lot of time reading and sleeping. The sun in Spain was far more powerful than what he was accustomed to in the Midwest. After a couple of days of near second-degree sunburns, he veered towards the shadier spots on the beach. *Well, if I am ever subject to the death penalty, it may not be radically different from these sunburns. I feel quite well poached from the Spanish sun.*

Fortunately, cooking in the sun did not attract any cannibals. Most likely, Spanish beaches are not their primary modus operandi.

Despite his limited exposure during this time, it was a gorgeous beach. The azure blue of the water was breathtaking, and the sand had an appealing visual symmetry. Sand dunes were nicely spaced out along the beach, and a few children built an impressive sand castle during his third day on the beach.

After eleven days of beach lounging, he was beginning to have dreams and flashbacks of the hectic streets of Paris. *That lifestyle is more appealing than being a beach idler. Too much relaxation loses its value after a while. I appreciate relaxation the most in small doses when it can be contrasted with the busy pace of life. I am very close to the saturation point; these days on the beach are now quite monotonous. Hectic urban life will no longer be a dream when I reach London. It will be exhilarating!*

Upon arriving in London, Thomas's heartbeat didn't race as it had when he first glimpsed Paris. It now felt akin to looking at ten artistic paintings at once rather than fifty. However, a more apt analogy, up here, was viewing ten stock prices simultaneously. London hummed with a much more business-like rhythm. Its francophone rival across the English Channel was definitely more of an art haven. Paris had been his first exposure to a very large city. Since he had been able to adapt in Paris after a few days, London now felt as though it were part of the same continuum.

As he walked through the streets of London to his youth hostel, he noticed how odd it felt to hear nearly everyone conversing in English. He remembered Winston Churchill's famous comment about the United States and Britain being two nations that were separated by a common language. In France, he had grown accustomed to being able to zone out conversations around him. Although he had learned some French in his language classes, it still required ample concentration to actually understand the conversations. Here, zoning out the conversations was much more difficult. Thomas had lost some privacy by being a native speaker of their language. *I am sure that many people will still regard me as the "dumb American", but it will be more challenging to "play dumb" when I can comprehend more of the interactions. How lovely that I will be able to fully comprehend the insults that will be lobbed at me. I was deprived of quite a bit of pleasure not fully understanding the insults in France. There I was, back in Plato's dark cave again, ignorant of the completeness of my American foolishness. I never studied Gödel's incompleteness theorem, but would it shed any light on this lack of full awareness regarding all of the insults that I missed?*

Thomas was content to observe that the drivers seemed to let him cross more easily on the crosswalks. *Possibly here they would object to Paul's driving. The traffic seems to flow at a more reasonable pace. Pedestrian insurance, if it existed, would be cheaper here.*

After he checked into his youth hostel room, he crashed and took a nap for a couple of hours. When he awoke, a couple of Irish men were enjoying a six-pack of beer in the room. One of them asked him if he would like a beer.

"I think that I will save drinking for later," he said sheepishly.

"What brings you to London?"

"I am interviewing for a position teaching English in Japan. I was in France for a little while, and then I relaxed for ten days on a Spanish beach. And yourself?"

"It's my first time here in the U.K., actually. We hear so much about the English in our history books that I wanted to see the place with my own eyes. I've traveled in several European countries though."

"Isn't this also Europe?" Thomas asked.

"Technically, you could say that, but we tend to refer to Europe as the Continent. We're islands over here; we feel separated from what we consider to be Europe."

"I see; I would not have picked that up in my history classes back home in the United States. Have you been to Paris as well?"

"Indeed I have."

"How would you compare London to Paris?"

"I would say London is more masculine. It's known for high finance. Paris emphasizes the arts a bit more and has a more feminine feel. They are often thought of as brother and sister cities, but they definitely have distinct differences. Paris has more cafés and not as many pubs. But the pubs here make me feel a bit closer to home," he said with a smile. "My friend and I are going to have some dinner. Would you care to join us?"

"Yes, I would. My name's Thomas, by the way."

"We have plenty of those in Ireland. I'm Patrick, and this is my friend Quinn. We were just going to eat at a traditional English pub a couple of streets away on Highgate Road. That might be a good first meal for you in London."

After a short walk to the pub, Thomas browsed the menu. It was obvious that the food was generally less interesting here at this pub compared to France, which he was expecting. He had never heard of anyone traveling to England for the food. He also recalled the "European vacation" joke again that he had first remembered at the airport in Bordeaux. According to the joke, the worst European vacation involved having a British person responsible for the cooking. This was definitely more "meat and potatoes cuisine" compared to France. He did notice an item on the menu called Yorkshire pudding, which he had never heard of before.

"Are you familiar with Yorkshire pudding?"

"That's a famous English dish. It has batter as a base with eggs and milk, and they often fill it with beef and gravy. It's mighty good. You should try it," Quinn said.

"Thanks, I might as well sample something unique. I'm not aware of a lot of unique dishes here, so I will take advantage of this opportunity."

"It's a bit more familiar to us. Our food is pretty much the same although Irish is of course better!" Quinn added with a wide, open-teeth smile.

"Are you a fan of *The Wire*?" Patrick asked.

"No, I'm not deeply familiar. You know about that show in Ireland?" Thomas asked.

"You'd be amazed how much American television we watch," he replied.

"And why is that? Why do you watch a lot of American television?"

"Well, when you're from a small country, you can't churn out so many television shows, lad. It forces ye to look across the ocean for some other options. For better or worse, that's how we learn about America. *The Wire*'s fecking brilliant!"

Thomas understood him for the most part, apart from some unusual words that he was not accustomed to hearing. *No two countries speak English exactly in the same way; that is obvious. Each place adapts the language to their culture, just as we have regional variations of English in the United States. It is quite plausible that I would have just as much difficulty understanding the English of an American from the Deep South.*

Quinn took a few sips of beer and then said, "I'm impressed that you haven't mentioned anything about the Irish and alcohol yet; I'm very accustomed to foreigners making jokes about our drinking. You're different from the other American lads I chatted with back home."

"You can say that again. I've known that I was very different since I fell out of the crib."

"Well, you'll be alright. The Wire is about drugs and gang life in Baltimore. It sometimes reminds me of the troubles of Ireland's past."

Thomas pondered his comment for a few moments. "Hmmm…I'm from rural Indiana, which is a few universes away from Baltimore. They probably have more black people on one street in Baltimore than in my entire county."

"We don't have many black people in Ireland either. The U.K. has more since many Afro-Caribbeans have immigrated here. Do you suppose that black people avoid places that start with 'I'?" Quinn said with a wink.

"Your theory may have some merit. Unfortunately, one glaring exception is the state of Illinois, which has a huge black population in Chicago."

"I'm just farting around. We like to do that in Ireland."

"It smells quite nice in here for someone who is farting around."

"Ah, you're the lad of the humorous jibes, you are. I like your imagination. It does smell nice. Our food has arrived."

Thomas did find the Yorkshire pudding to be appetizing. The texture was different than anything that he had tasted in the United States (or certainly France, for that matter). It didn't have the rich flavors of French cuisine, but it was tasty nonetheless. He was expecting any kind of "English" food to be nauseatingly bad. Since he had started from that baseline of expectations, the Yorkshire pudding was a pleasant surprise. It was a hearty meal. He was able to order apple juice here instead of wine without feeling humiliated. He did not yearn for that aspect of his French experience. Quinn managed to guzzle down three beers during the meal while Thomas sipped his apple juice. *When I go into these youth hostels, I must have a sign on me that says: "Heavy drinkers, come chat with this guy who can't hold his liquor." I need to explain to them that I'm not Prometheus. If Zeus eats my liver during the day, it's not going to be replenished at night. They are fortunate that they think that they are more like Prometheus. Either that or they just don't care that much about their livers. That is a definite possibility.*

Twenty minutes later, they returned to the youth hostel. After the flight and the visual bombardment of a new city, he had very little energy left. Thomas decided to have a very low-key evening. Morrissey may have sung about "panic on the streets of London", but Thomas wouldn't be able to experience it tonight. He would have to settle for thinking about it vicariously from his youth hostel room.

The interview was about thirty minutes from his youth hostel by subway, or the Tube, as it was called in London. Thomas observed that the subway in London was in much shabbier condition than the one in Paris. The tracks were in much poorer condition, and the train cars seemed to be from a more ancient era. He recalled from his history classes that the French favored greater state involvement compared to the British. There were few equivalents in British history of the Sun King, and the Industrial Revolution mostly started in Britain, which laid a strong foundation for private enterprise. *Possibly higher taxes are a fair trade for a more reliable, cutting-edge subway. It never feels great to lose significant amounts of my paycheck to taxes, but using a dilapidated subway doesn't seem to be terribly advisable either. There truly is no free lunch. If I make a small gain in the river waters, I get compensated with a corresponding loss somewhere else.* They kept announcing on the speaker to "mind the gap". *The main gap that I mind is the gap in quality between this subway train and the ones that I took in Paris! I don't think that singing the praises of France will make me popular here though.*

Thomas also felt quite unique today because he had never worn a suit before. *Wearing a suit makes me feel quite important; I feel much more important than I am. From the perspective of the universe, I'm a speck of dust. From the perspective of the U.K., I'm one person among millions. Even from the perspective of the subway, I'm quite insignificant. Yet this suit makes me feel powerful and worth something; look at me with these fancy pants and expensive clothes that I could not afford to buy! I bought them anyway so that my appearance would appear to be "professional" for this position. Ron, back at the bookstore, described this job as being similar to a "professional talking monkey". If I were only a talking monkey, now that would be the horror to end all horrors! But if I were a professional talking monkey?? Now my life is leading a righteous path!*

The interview was a short walk from the Tube station. The weather was quite cloudy and gray, with a light drizzling rain. He had been warned before to have an umbrella at all times in England; the place was not known for abundant sunshine. *No wonder they say that the sun never sets on the British Empire. There never was any sun to begin with!*

He entered a large building with seventeen floors. *My parents would fall out of their chairs if they entered a building with this many floors. There just isn't enough corn in small-town Indiana to fill up so much office space.* He was five minutes early for the interview; he had timed the trip well. When he entered the suite on the fifth floor, a very young-looking, small Japanese girl was present at the front desk.

"Good morning. Can I have your name?" she said in a very

gentle, sweet voice.

"Thomas Gephardt."

"Yes. Mr. Yamamoto will be with you soon," she said with a smile and a slight bow of her head.

She definitely smiles more than most of the French. They seem to be a bit more courteous when they first greet you here. Yamamoto sounds like a great name for a car. I do not think that I will mention that during the interview though. If the French had extreme difficulty understanding my humor, there is little reason to think that it will be significantly easier for the Japanese. I prefer not to get off on the wrong foot (in the car) as soon as the interview begins.

Mr. Yamamoto arrived exactly on time in the lobby to take Thomas to his interview room. *He seems to keep time precisely. Technically, he is ten seconds late, but I will not mention this to him either. I do not know enough about the culture to determine which comment would be the bigger insult; would he be more offended hearing that his last name would be a good name for a car, or hearing that he is ten seconds late? If I wind up going to Japan, hopefully I will be able to answer this question when I have spent more time there.* Mr. Yamamoto was dressed in an extremely well-pressed suit. His hair was extremely precisely combed. *I do not think that I can find one wrinkle on his clothing. If he wanted his suit to match his age well, it should at least have a few wrinkles. Another random thought that I will refrain from mentioning.*

"Pleased to meet you, Thomas. Come this way, please."

They went down a long hallway into one of the interview rooms.

"Have seat, please. I have your resume here. My first question: why do you want to teach in Japan?"

Hmm...I mostly want to explore Asian culture, and teaching English seems to be one of the easiest means of achieving this end. However, this does not sound like a great answer to his question.

"I enjoy sharing my knowledge with others. When I was a university student, I participated in a tutoring program and I found this to be very satisfying. Teaching in Japan would add another dimension of sharing my culture with another nation. I am also very interested in languages; I recently learned French, and I believe that it would be a wonderful opportunity to learn Japanese. I believe that I would learn more about my own language by attempting to teach it to others."

Mr. Yamamoto had a very dispassionate countenance while he was listening to Thomas. Thomas was unable to tell if Mr. Yamamoto liked his response. *I feel quite a large distance from him. A lot of the French projected formality and distance as well, but it still felt different than this. It felt closer to reserve with many of the French; with Mr. Yamamoto, on the other hand, I feel that we are on completely different wavelengths. It's almost as if we're on different planets despite the fact that we are sitting at the same table! Let's see if this feeling continues during the interview.*

"How do you feel about rule? Do you see it as flexible, or do you think that it is very important to follow rule and policy?"

This is an obvious trap. Only a fool would answer that he sees company rules as flexible. How dumb does he think that I am? Yes, Mr. Yamamoto, I'm an American cowboy who's going to shoot up the school if there are any rules that annoy me. I'm going to finish the job that we started in 1945 and establish a full-blown American colony instead of merely imposing martial law. Good thing that you caught me before I was able to sneak into Japan as a subversive English teacher!

"I think that it is very important to follow the rules. Employers have reasons for their rules, and it helps to establish a more harmonious work environment if the rules are respected."

I'm ready for your next totally BS question. As they used to say on the TV Show You Can't Do That on Television, *"Ready, Aim, Fire!"*

"How would you feel in classroom of student who do not speak? Student is very quiet. What do you do?"

Okay, this is a much more legitimate question, I do have to admit. I gather that he is trying to give me some idea about the conditions of the position and see how I respond to different situations. They must not use a lot of plurals in Japanese. I do not think that I have heard him use any plurals yet.

"I would call on specific students if nobody volunteers to speak. I would ask them direct questions. Hopefully this will open up class discussion."

Mr. Yamamoto's eyebrows twitched slightly in response. This was about the closest that Thomas could find to a physical reaction to his speech.

"Okay, please ask me question that you might ask student in conversation class."

"Mr. Yamamoto, what is your favorite food?"

"Sushi."

"Why do you like sushi?"

"It taste good."

"How often do you eat sushi?"

"Okay, I see that you will try to make conversation with student. I want you see that it can be hard work if student is quiet. Please do not think of this job as easy one."

"Yes, I understand that it would be a challenging job."

"Do you have question that you want ask?"

"How many classes would I be teaching?"

"Each class is fifty minute. You teach between thirty and thirty-five class each week. There is no teaching on Japanese holiday and you receive eight other paid day of vacation in one-year contract."

"How is the housing done by the company?"

"We give you small apartment and take out rent from your check. Apartment in Japan is usually very small. Our country is very crowded."

"When do you expect to inform candidates about their status?"

"About one week after interview. We are very large company and we interview very often. Can you live only in Tokyo, or can you go to any place in Japan?"

"I am open to most locations. It doesn't have to be Tokyo."

Mr. Yamamoto faintly smiled upon hearing this statement. *Perhaps I have increased my chances at getting the position by being flexible about location.*

"Any other question?"

"Those are my main questions. Thank you for your time, Mr. Yamamoto."

"You are welcome. Here is my business card. Thank you."

Thomas took the business card with one hand and stuffed it into his pocket.

Immediately after doing this, he heard a strong sucking-in-the-lips sound. *I did not see any noodles on the table, so why is Mr. Yamamoto doing this?* However, within the context, he could sense that Mr. Yamamoto was a little bit irritated. *Aha. Most likely, I have committed another cultural faux pas. Too bad that this did not happen in Japan; then I could claim to have committed a faux pas on two continents! If I get the position, I am sure that I will have plenty of opportunities to commit more faux pas over there. It is so easy to do in a foreign culture. How can one know all of the cultural intricacies and subtleties of every place? At one point they tried to develop a universal language called Esperanto, he recalled. We need a universal culture to avoid all of these humiliating mistakes in foreign lands. Though what would be the pleasure of travel if culture was universal? No, these faux pas are a very small price to pay for the tremendous rewards of immersion in foreign cultures.*

Analyzing the issue more optimistically, couldn't I argue that the faux pas are part of the entertainment aspect? If a faux pas causes a punch to my face or I get severely beaten, then that is a quite different case. However, if they are relatively harmless ones such as the ones that I have committed so far, I should look at them in a much more positive light. Because of my faux pas in the French restaurant in Bordeaux, I learned about the vital importance of wine in French culture. Now, due to my faux pas with Mr. Yamamoto, I have gained knowledge about the value of business cards in Japanese culture. I do not know exactly what my faux pas was. But with a minimal amount of research or discussions with people familiar with Japan, it would be quite straightforward to find out the true nature of my error. I hope that this error will not disqualify me from the position. Mr. Yamamoto interviews foreigners constantly though. Surely at least one other person has made this mistake? I might be unique, but I'm not unique to that extreme; this would be a quite likely faux pas to commit. Most likely, Mr. Yamamoto has seen this faux pas before, but because what I did is contrary to how he was molded in his culture, it still draws a somewhat strong reaction from him. In fact, that was the most intense emotion that I felt from him during the entire interview! He mostly just went through the motions, asking questions and showing little response to my answers. But when I perform an act with his business card that is against his cultural practice, then all hell breaks loose! Well, if I obtain this position, possibly he will write in my file: "Professional talking monkey is qualified to teach. But do not give the monkey any business cards. They will be found next to the banana peels on the floor in his cage."

Now Thomas was in a waiting stage. He realized that it was never wise to put all of his eggs in one basket, but how many

Japanese language schools were interviewing in London? *This is harsh, being in limbo. It is as if I am submerged in an intermediate state of matter between a solid and a liquid, or between a liquid and a gas. A defined state of matter assures some kind of stability. Even a gas knows how "it" will behave. But I do not know what my next steps will be in this comedy of the absurd called life. Not having a defined state of matter is causing me a lot of angst. What will I do if I am not offered the position? Search for a teaching job in Japan from Indiana? I definitely would like to attempt teaching in Japan. It came to me in a flash of inspiration in the bookstore, and now that the genie is out of the bottle, it seems to be completely unattainable to put it back in. Once the bottle of wine is uncorked, it can never go back to its former state. That is how I see my previous state before I realized that the next step in this travel journey is to teach in Japan.*

I am not religious, but somehow I feel that I was meant to meet those Aussie guys in Paris who knew about Japan. I cannot prove it mathematically or show any scientific evidence that would support this assertion. It is merely an impulse that I feel from my heart. That meeting was meant to happen. Hopefully this also means that I will be offered this position, assuming that Mr. Yamamoto does recover from my business card tomfoolery.

Although there is certainly a large amount of asymmetry between how I perceive the event and how Mr. Yamamoto must have seen it, I prefer to chuckle that he became so distraught over a business card! Yet to him, this seemed to be an event of intense trauma. What is a business card anyway? Is it rational to be so attached to a card that has my position, email, and phone number? Possibly Mr. Yamamoto defines himself largely by his job? At this point in life, I merely see a job as a way to pay my bills, for the most part. I do not attach it to my identity in the kind of way that I would become emotionally attached to an inanimate business card. Just as Mr. Yamamoto's suit was so immaculately clean and pressed, he seems to see his business card in a similar light. It was as if by stuffing the card into my pocket too haphazardly, I wrinkled his suit. I should have brought an iron to the interview! After my faux pas, I should have taken the business card out and ironed it. That would have set everything right. I also could have offered to iron his suit while he was wearing it as a conciliatory gesture. If he were witty, he would respond to such an offer by saying, "You're playing with fire when you make such offers." I do not think that Mr. Yamamoto would have said that. He probably would have just made that hissing and sucking sound again as if he were eating ten bowls of noodles and replied, "No, thank you." Perhaps when people are in Hell, they are required to iron their clothes while wearing them. At least it is efficient; people can skip the step of putting on their neatly pressed clothing. I remember hearing guys back in college talk about feeling "the burn" while weightlifting at the gym. Well, that is a quite weak way of feeling the burn compared to my proposed ironing method! Those guys prided themselves on their toughness, but could they endure this ironing method? Probably not; they are content with baby burns.

Thomas decided to spend most of his spare time by diving into history. There were numerous opportunities in London to explore this interest. The British Museum was full of plundered items from other lands. He spent a couple of days at the traditional monuments, such as Westminster Abbey and St. Paul's Cathedral. *This society oozes royalty. The Monarchy is a fundamental part of their identity. As Americans, we came onto the scene too late, relatively speaking, to have that kind of identity. They might speak the same language as us, but that is certainly one fundamental distinction. There have been quasi-royal families in the United States, such as the Kennedys, Rockefellers, etc. But quasi-royal is all that they can ever be. It cannot compare to the entrenched, ancient institution of monarchy.*

In the United States, we admire characters such as Huckleberry Finn. We marvel at their adventurousness wading down the Mississippi River. Huck is esteemed next to the tough gunslingers of the West and the determined cowboys who tamed the land down in Texas. It is virtually impossible to see those prototypes being idolized in this society. How could a cowboy emerge here? Everything seems to be so crowded and densely populated; a lot of pubs would have to be destroyed and razed to make those cowboy conditions possible. Without a doubt, the vastness of American spaces in certain parts of the country has profoundly influenced the identity of those spaces.

Once again, Thomas saw the power of travel for understanding history. He could spend years within American libraries reading about the history of westward expansion and cowboys in Texas. But it would be extremely difficult to be able to grasp the unique American nature of these characters unless he left American borders. Within a couple days of observing historical monuments in cramped British conditions, the thought-provoking contrast of the two nations flashed before his eyes. Einstein had become famous by developing a theory about the relativistic nature of frames of reference in the scientific realm. This idea had some relevance to the human realm as well. Once again, he was back to Plato's allegory of the cave. *I cannot thoroughly analyze my frame of reference until I am outside of it. Within my American frame of reference, Texas cowboys seem so matter of fact. It is natural for people to react with "so what?" So what if there were cowboys in this state?* But now he, as a traveler, was able to see that they were, to a large degree, products of their geography. It was not a matter of completely unbounded human free will or human imagination that produced these entities. Geography and the physical land set these wheels into motion.

The days went by, exploring various aspects of London's history and eating more pub food. He was becoming a mini-expert on fish and chips as well as feeling congested in his aorta. *It's too bad that all of this oil that I am eating could not power a car. Gas is quite expensive here. If only there were a way to make use of the buckets of oil that I ingest every time I order fish and chips. It's a good thing that I won't be continuing to eat fish and chips so much; otherwise Cardiologist John Buckingham Westminster Smith would have a serious patient soon. Fried food establishments should have to pay commissions to cardiologists; they give them a lot of business.*

Although he was quite engrossed in London's history and pub food, it was nonetheless in the back of his mind that he had not yet heard from Gova, the Japanese language school. It was becoming more difficult to fall asleep at night, as he wondered about his future. In his darker moments, he was thinking that it was likely that he might have to return to the United States to plot his next move. Then the phone call came. He had been accepted for a position. Not only that, but he would be teaching in Kyoto, which was the old capital of Japan. The Gova employee told him that he was lucky to be placed there; Kyoto was filled with hundreds of traditional Japanese temples.

He was also informed that he had the choice of his own company-provided apartment or sharing with a couple of room-mates. His rent would be much cheaper if he chose the second option. He did not need a lot of time to consider these options. He thought that it would be wiser to have roommates. He had never lived by himself, and he was not quite ready to attempt it for the first time in a different culture. It would also be more economical to split living costs with roommates. Sure, there was some risk that he might have conflicts with his roommates. But he also knew that if he lived alone, he was virtually guaranteed to struggle with loneliness. *Whom will I debate at the dinner table if I live alone? Myself? Sure, I'll have a split personality and debate myself. No, debating an actual person is probably preferable.*

Thomas asked how soon he could start the position, and the employee said that there was an option to start his training within two weeks. He replied that he wanted to start as soon as possible. The employee said that he would provide more details in a few days, and that Thomas should book his flight now.

Living in Asia would soon be a reality. This caused a strong flame to kindle inside him. He could not remember the last time in his life that he felt this ebullient about the future. In general, he did not become enthusiastic easily. However, this was a significant milestone. *I am now becoming a true blooded adventurer. There are loads of Americans who spend some time in Europe. But a much smaller percentage ever set foot in Asia. This should be quite eye-opening (and possibly nose-opening as well if the food is unusual at all). If I vomit from being unfamiliar with the food, it will be stomach-opening as well. However, I would prefer that the stomach experience is more constricting. Generally, stomach-opening experiences are not particularly enjoyable.*

He decided that he would return to the Spanish beach in Majorca until it was time to leave. It was much cheaper to be there compared to London. He had appreciated soaking in the British historical sights, but he did not have the financial resources to remain in London for two more weeks. Even the youth hostels in London averaged around $25 per night. The high cost of food and transport were also quickly draining his pocketbook. He calculated that even after booking the cost of a flight to Spain, it would still be more economical to spend the next couple of weeks there. *This travel bug stretches my wallet at least as much as my mind. World travel is certainly not for the poor and destitute; it is an economic privilege, which is unfortunate. Our wallets severely constrict our possibilities; this is an unavoidable fact of this harsh reality. From a global perspective, I am much wealthier than the majority of the globe. The majority of the world's inhabitants cannot sojourn on a Spanish beach for two weeks, and they certainly are prohibited from sightseeing in London.* Even though he lamented that he was unable to see more of England, he thought that it was essential to keep these global realities in perspective.

Time passed quickly in Majorca. His situation felt analogous to being stuck in traffic; he was predominantly focused on the next highway exit. His mind was entirely consumed by curiosity: what would the streets in Japan look like? What kinds of fashion styles would he observe? Would he see any wrinkled suits, or would they all have the spotless appearance of Mr. Yamamoto's suit? How would he feel about Japanese women? He had never met any Japanese women in the United States. Day and night, endless questions bombarded his psyche. He had not had any experiences to prepare himself for the next voyage. This was his first endeavor leaving the borders of Western civilization.

He fully realized that he should not overestimate the exotic nature of this journey. He was not traveling to an extremely destitute nation where he would lack electricity, running water, or technology. He was still traveling to an advanced, fully industrialized nation. Yet this fact did not totally soothe his nerves; it was an inescapable point that he would be living in a very foreign culture. From his general knowledge of history, he was fully aware that Japan had a quite distinct history from the West. Therefore, it seemed to be inevitable that these historical experiences would influence the cultural practices. He knew that Japan had a history of unique "characters" that were not found in the West, such as geishas and samurai warriors. *I hope to see at least a few geishas when I am there. My experience will not feel complete unless I get to experience this aspect of the culture in some way.*

Growing up, when he thought of the Japanese, the first image that entered his mind was Mr. Miyagi from *The Karate Kid.* "Wax on, wax off, Daniel-san." Who could fail to recall this scene? But he was sophisticated enough at this point in life to know that this was a caricature in a Hollywood movie. How much did this scene really explain about Japanese culture? It explained very little. He would have to see the "real" Japan to gain any cultural understanding. Hollywood stereotypes and caricatures were not a suitable means towards this end. However, they were a splendid means towards learning how to wax a car brilliantly! He could not view cars in the same light after watching the film; every speck of dirt stood out and needed to be waxed over. Possibly someone had "waxed on and waxed off" Mr. Yamamoto's suit before he met Thomas that day? Was that why it was so immaculate looking?

5

Chapter Five

November 2015

When it was time to leave, Thomas psychologically prepared himself for another long flight. In fact, this journey was going to be twice as long as the flight between the U.S. and France. He had a short flight to Barcelona followed by a transfer in Helsinki, Finland. Then, on a flight with Japan Airlines, he would fly to Osaka. The company representative from Gova informed him that a company official would pick him up at the Osaka airport and drive him to his apartment in Kyoto.

This will be my second time being greeted at a foreign airport. I am becoming similar to a Hollywood star, though without the income to match. How many rich Hollywood stars have been chauffeured out of airports in France and Japan? Surely there must be a program entitled "Lifestyles of the Quasi-Rich and the Quasi-Famous" in which I could be a participant? However, if I were to appear on this program, this would possibly be distorting the meaning of the term "quasi". Quasi usually implies some resemblance to the term in which it is matched. However, I am nowhere close to attaining wealth or fame. Is there another program called "Lifestyles of the (Extremely not) Rich and the (Extremely not) Famous"? This could be a worthy subject for discussion next time that I bump into another group of travelers at a youth hostel; surely it will happen again.

When he boarded his connecting flight in Helsinki, he observed that half of the passengers were Japanese. He only was familiar with a few basic Japanese words, but he was able to discern that spoken Japanese sounded very soft and rhythmical. He noticed that most of the Japanese passengers were quite small. He had never felt big from a physical perspective in the United States or in Europe, but now, he suddenly felt large, comparatively speaking. *Possibly this flight will be slightly more comfortable if the other passengers have smaller builds. My imagined photographer will be able to magnify my presence and reduce cropping.*

Apparently in addition to being a talking monkey in Japan, he was going to be a *giant* talking monkey. If any of his students were expecting to learn English from a baby talking monkey, then they had purchased the wrong ticket. These English lessons would now have much greater authority coming from a giant. Like an authoritative, muscular general, he would whip the students into shape and have them speaking inspiring, expressive English very quickly. Then he woke up from his psychotic delusion.

There were several young Japanese women on the plane. He also noticed that a couple of the women on the plane had applied extremely large quantities of makeup. He had never observed cosmetics at this level in France. He thought that many French women enhanced their beauty with a "reasonable" level of makeup, but he thought that these Japanese women were taking a possibly good idea to an unwise extreme. *What is the appearance of these women beneath these pools of makeup? Would they even recognize themselves in the mirror? When they put on this much makeup, it is analogous to a Kafka-like metamorphosis.*

Now he strongly wished that he could speak Japanese; he wanted to tell one of them that they were living the real-life version of Kafka's Metamorphosis. *They will probably understand this comment as thoroughly as the French received most of my jokes. Regardless of which country I plant my shoes in, I am pretty much condemned to making offbeat comments and then receiving blank stares of confusion in return. People in Indiana rarely understood my jokes either. In that case, I blamed it on their education levels rather than a language barrier. It is more comforting to attribute the gap in understanding to a language barrier because it suggests that there is at least potential for them to understand me if we had enough linguistic common ground. When people in my own country give the same blank stares of bewilderment in response to my jokes, it is a much deeper feeling of estrangement. I never lost hope in France that eventually I could understand them and eventually they could understand me, if there were enough time to understand the nuances of the culture and become fluent in the language. However, in Indiana, my hope of common understanding with my fellow countrymen never went beyond the "extremely futile" phase.*

If noise could fill a balloon, then the balloons on this flight were much smaller than the previous ones. The Japanese spoke at very low volumes. On the flight to Paris, both the Europeans and the Americans contributed to the boisterousness. He had recalled that a couple of American ladies behind him on that flight spoke so loudly that it felt as if they were right next to him, shouting into his ear the intimate details of their pedestrian lives. *I could have been a scholar about the specials at Macy's and JC Penney if I had wished after that flight. Fortunately, eventually, the blabbermouth ladies did fall asleep. Even they eventually ran out of gas, and I was able to return to some psychological serenity. Too much chatter disrupts my mental equilibrium. Simon and Garfunkel's song "The Sound of Silence" foreshadowed my mental disposition quite well.*

At one point, Thomas stood up to use the bathroom. When he saw that it was occupied, he waited for a few minutes in the aisle. After the white man who was using the bathroom left, he walked towards the door, but at the same time, a Japanese lady using the restroom left as well. She nearly bumped into him. Her expression froze, and her eyes looked very startled.

"Eto...soooooo sorry," she said with a bow. Then she walked away.

That is a unique apology! I've never heard someone drag out the word "so" that long. She might have a future as an opera singer, if she has a good singing voice. Was it really rational to drag out this word so long during an apology? Had the lady really committed a heinous act? She had almost bumped into him by mistake, which seemed to be a quite small error on the grand scale of things. *If this is a "normal" type of response to this situation in Japan, then this is definitely not the most logical culture.* He had remembered how courteous the Japanese receptionist was at his interview back in London. This second interaction seemed to be continuing this trend of extreme courtesy. Yes, extreme politeness seemed to be at the forefront of this culture, which did not suit Thomas particularly well. *I feel a sizable wall from someone when they are too polite. Too much politeness and formality creates barriers and to me feels simply not genuine. The world is a coarse and bumpy place; this is why this extreme courtesy seems so alien to me.*

Once again, he yearned for that elusive, reasonable middle. He did not enjoy his experience in the hotel in France when the man yelled and screamed at him, and then consoled him that he was still better than the Algerians. On the other hand, disproportionate politeness made him recoil almost as much. Both actions were examples of deviations from what he saw as a reasonable middle ground. He actually did like Paul quite a bit from this perspective. He had not thought that Paul was particularly insolent, nor did he practice an extreme courteousness. He was an engaging conversationalist, and Thomas had not felt large artificial walls when conversing with him. *Engaging conversation is much more meaningful to me than overdone courtesy. The punishment has to fit the crime, lady. You made me feel worse by being overly contrite for a trivial offense. You made me feel as if I somehow caused you a large amount of remorse from such a petty matter. The irony of this situation is that your extreme level of courteousness made me feel worse, not better. This should be part of the rationale behind Aristotle's reasonable middle. If the logic of the response does not fit the situation, then the intention is likely to cause unintended consequences, which is not desirable. There has to be some logic that underpins the symmetry of human relationships. Otherwise, we are merely living in a world of madness. Is my plane headed towards a world of madness? I will soon find out in the upcoming months.*

Returning to his seat, he observed that the first meal was coming soon. Young, fit flight attendants were wheeling the meals down the aisle. All of the flight attendants appeared to be relatively young; he doubted that any were over the age of thirty-five. *Does this airline discriminate based on age? It must be so; it does not make sense otherwise that all of the flight attendants would be young. Surely, older women in Japan needed jobs as well. Also, they are all relatively attractive.*

Now a flight attendant had arrived at his row.

"Good afternoon. Would you like pork or chicken?" she asked with a smile, showing her small mouth. Her tone of voice was very formal and courteous; it was quite different than how he was used to being addressed in France. *Already I miss the more "natural" way that they spoke in France, and I haven't even set foot yet on Japanese soil! With any luck, I shall find some other aspects of the culture in Japan redeeming. It seems highly improbable that I will dislike the culture in its entirety. The yins have to get balanced out by the yangs, and vice versa. Perhaps I should ask her if she is "soooooo sorry" that I am having difficulty adjusting to the formal Japanese way of speaking.*

"I would like pork."

She handed him his lunch with both hands underneath the food, even though it was a very small container. *This is likely another example of their formalism? Only we uncivilized barbarians in the West use one hand to hand over food. With a bit of luck, my lunch will taste better now that both of your holy hands gave it to me.* He then considered that possibly this was far from an ideal attitude when entering a foreign land. *Many aspects of the culture will be unfamiliar; I need to attempt to adjust to my new reality with a mixture of flexibility and a positive sense of humor.*

Becoming defensive towards everything that is out of my comfort zone is a very quick route to misery. Why travel such a lengthy distance with this attitude? Suppose that it is true that some Japanese people would find it offensive if I handed something to them with one hand (or put their business card in my pocket). Are they automatically incorrect? Possibly they see the practice of using two hands as a sign of respect? Possibly to them, this respect is more important than being "natural", whatever that means. Perhaps to them, this extreme formalism is "natural"; it is part of the customs that they have been raised with and are expected to observe. Couldn't they argue that Western-style bluntness and informality is also "unnatural"?

He considered that the root meaning of the term "natural"

meant "to occur in nature". But indisputably, not everything in nature was virtuous. Observing a lion in the jungle chasing after smaller animals and eating their flesh was one hundred percent "natural", but it did not seem to be honorable. Thomas suddenly realized that his argument about something being "natural" seemed to be merely a cover for advocating that something was more comfortable for him. But on what grounds could he objectively say that he was right and that the Japanese were wrong? *Travel continues to teach me how subjective this world is. I have every right to feel more comfortable with how most of the French people spoke to me, but the Japanese have an equal right to feel much more at ease with their culture. I am under no obligation to deeply love Japan or its culture. However, I cannot pedantically condemn them as mistaken or second-rate merely for having dissimilar cultural practices. If I insist on this course of action, then I am no better than the "ugly Americans" in Indiana whom I have fled from on this long flight.*

His meal was some kind of breaded pork. It was served with a burgundy-colored sauce. It tasted unlike any other pork that he had ever eaten; the meat itself tasted a bit different. *It is possible that they have different farming practices, which will influence the meat's flavor.* Furthermore, he generally hadn't seen pork breaded in this manner. He was more accustomed to seeing breaded chicken (chicken tenders) in the United States. He would later learn that this dish was called tonkatsu. The seasonings were pretty lightly applied; he did not feel that it was bland, but it did not have an extremely rich flavor either. *I should not expect the elaborate seasonings that I adored in France. I have never heard that Japan is particularly famous for its food other than sushi; it should be quite appealing to eat sushi in its original country.* Regardless, he felt nostalgic for Marie's home-cooked meals. She would have seasoned this pork quite a bit more heavily to give it a richer flavor. *I wish that I could text her to let her know that I am thinking about her food on the plane. Hopefully, she would take it as a flattering comment that I am thinking about her food while I am hundreds of miles away, nearly knocking over Japanese ladies on my way to the bathroom.*

The tonkatsu was also served with a small salad. The salad was mostly lettuce with a few carrots thrown in and a ginger type dressing. He thought that the dressing was pretty tasty, though not extremely strong. He appreciated the more subtle flavor of this dressing compared to many American salads that were often drowning in fattening dressings. Especially at many of the chain restaurants in Indiana, the dressing was much more prominent than the salad itself. In these restaurants, it was more appropriate for the waitress to ask, "What kind of salad would you like with your dressing?" *I'd like the salad in a small cup on the side (of a huge plate drowning in dressing),* Thomas had always wanted to answer.

He had noticed that, in general, most of the Japanese people on the plane were quite slim. Thomas would not describe any of them as overweight. A few were "average" weight by American standards, but as a whole, they were significantly slimmer than his American compatriots in Indiana. *It is possible that less dressing is one of many contributing factors to these smaller waistlines. People have a tendency to think that if they eat salad, they are eating very healthily, and then they offset any gains from the greens by bludgeoning it with dressing.*

Although he enjoyed the subtle flavors of his meal on the whole, he struggled with the chopsticks. He considered asking for Western-style silverware, but he felt embarrassed to do so. It reminded him too much of his initial dining experience in

France, when he ordered apple juice instead of wine. Fitting in with foreign eating cultures is no small task, he realized anew. He had almost never used chopsticks in the United States, and his clumsy hand-eye coordination made this novel task considerably more challenging. Four or five times, he picked up pieces of the tonkatsu, and clumsy hand movements caused the pieces to fall back onto the plate. He was quite tempted at times to wonder why they enjoyed eating with this type of utensil, and then he remembered that he had to work towards being more tolerant of different customs. *Still, it seems so much more efficient to be able to stab the meat with a fork. Again, I seem to be finding Western customs more "efficient"; I found the French manner of speaking more efficient as well. They seemed to get to the point more quickly compared to the formal, courteous, more roundabout Japanese way of speaking. They must have some other kind of motivation besides efficiency for using chopsticks in Asia. When I am more settled at my apartment in Japan, I'm going to research the motivations for the development of this custom. It doesn't make sense that there would be no reason whatsoever for using these foreign (to Western eyes) chopsticks. Therefore, I merely need to research why they are used, and hopefully this will shed some light on their "efficiency" compared to Western silverware.*

After he had finished eating and satisfied his appetite, he considered trying to make conversation with the man next to him. This man was very well dressed. He appeared to be in his mid-forties, and he was wearing a neatly pressed black tie with his white dress shirt and black pants. He had a muted expression on his face as he was reading a Japanese newspaper. Thomas had noticed that this stoicism was a general trend among the Japanese whom he had seen so far. It was very difficult for him to have any clue about what they were thinking or how they were feeling. Very few of them seemed to display the range of facial expressions that he was used to from Westerners, such as expressing anger or sadness.

If one of them murders me, I don't think that I will be able to say that I saw it coming. Most likely, the person will simply have his courteous mild smile and then seconds later he pulls out his gun and shoots me. Or if he's nostalgic for the samurai era, he'll whip out his sword and plunge it into my guts, all while he has no expression on his face, as if he were just retrieving his mail. I never watched any of the Japanese samurai films before, but now I'm intrigued. This very brief exposure to Japanese culture in a London office and on an airplane makes me want to explore this stoic tendency in greater detail. How did the samurai behave and interact with one another? In a Western context, these kinds of warriors would be likely to come off as macho with strong emotions. Did the samurai ever break down emotionally? Possibly that is why they have a high suicide rate in Japan? They repress these emotions and put on stoic airs for eons, and then when it becomes unbearable, they kill themselves. Putting his Western cap back on, Thomas could only wonder: *isn't it better to release some bad emotions a little bit at a time, rather than releasing them through one big thrust with a sword to the belly? All evidence points to the fact that I am going to be living in an extreme place. On the scale of normality, this does not seem to be a society that hovers around the middle of the bell curve. No, I will be spending ample time on the tails of that curve. I will be astonished if this prediction turns out to be incorrect.*

This is interesting that I have developed this gut impression already without ever having set foot on Japanese soil. Who knew that I could formulate these hypotheses merely from a long, excruciating plane ride? When people discuss flying, it is mostly talked about in a negative context. People focus on the hassles of airport security, the long waits in the airport, and the discomfort while on the plane. But despite all of these unappealing features of the flying experience, I have turned it into an anthropological one, at least to my eyes. Japanese people, when you're on a plane with me, you can run but you cannot hide. Within the confines of this large object, you cannot avoid my theorizing and generalizing. Most of you probably have zero interest in my opinions about your culture. I would feel the same way about many foreigners' views of my culture. There is a natural tendency to recoil at criticism from others whom are outside of the culture. Criticism from other cultures usually is received as condescending or patronizing. I greatly sympathize with this frame of mind. However, I have not expressed any of my thoughts to the Japanese passengers on this plane. Is it a crime to theorize and generalize inside my own head? As Plato once said, the unexamined life is not worth living. If I cannot make generalizations about groups and cultures, even inside my own head, then this existence is far more burdensome than it is worth. That question does not entail any cost-benefit analysis. The costs are immense, and the benefits of not being able to generalize and theorize are nil.

Shifting his focus away from the tumultuous tsunami of his own mind and back towards the external world (which was extremely tranquil in comparison), he decided to talk to the stoic gentleman.

"Excuse me, sir, do you speak English?"

"Eto...some English."

"Do you mind if I ask you what is your job?"

He lightly smiled, and his eyebrows moved a minuscule amount.

"Product market."

"What kind of products?"

"Eto...I forget English word. Some technology."

"Do you live in Kyoto?"

"No. Osaka. Little company in Kyoto. Osaka has many company."

"I'll be teaching English in Kyoto. Do you think that I would be better off teaching in Osaka?"

"No understand. Please repeat."

"Do you think that Osaka is better than Kyoto?"

"Hai...yes...eto...Osaka is more business. Kyoto is tourist city. You can go to temple. Interesting with you. Sorry...English poor."

This conversation was better than I anticipated. At least he treated me with respect and he attempted to speak English to the best of his ability. I did not feel any condescension from him. That is a pleasant change from some of my more tense exchanges that I experienced in Europe. They seem to use this word "eto" a lot. From the context, it sounds like "hmm" in English. Thomas noticed that he had difficulty distinguishing the letters "r" and "l" during the conversation. *Yes, I seem to recall this issue with my Japanese classmate at the language school back in France as well. Most likely, they do not have such defined "r" and "l" sounds in the Japanese language. I had difficulty pronouncing some of the sounds in French, and that is much closer to English. It makes sense that a language that is from a distant family (and corner of the world) would have quite dissimilar sounds. No wonder that there are many more opportunities to teach English in Asia compared to Europe; it's much more work for the Asians to learn English. Europeans who speak English as a foreign language are fortunate in that regard; their native tongues are much more similar. It is no small feat to learn any language, but it must be especially arduous for the Asians. Well, the stereotype is that they have a very resilient work ethic. Assuming that this stereotype is grounded in reality, it should aid their abilities to become fluent in English. Otherwise, it would be quite a task to master extremely unrelated phonetic sounds.*

He also found the man's comments about Osaka compared to Kyoto noteworthy. Apparently, Osaka was more of a business-oriented city and Kyoto was filled with temples and other tourist attractions. *It will be magnificent to have such close proximity to all of these Japanese temples. This will be a tremendous opportunity for soaking in the culture.* He also knew from previous conversations with Gova employees that Kyoto was the old imperial capital of Japan; therefore, it was also a first-rate opportunity to continue exploring history in action. *Eventually, with enough travel, my mind is going to become an extensive kaleidoscope of historical memories. Japanese temples will merge effortlessly with French cathedrals, English abbeys and other remains from unexplored (as of this date) societies. When a person becomes well-traveled, it is akin to being a casual cultural anthropologist. I may lack the formal academic methods of study that go along with academic cultural anthropology, but I am still without question in their realm. I am studying diverse human behaviors that are often steeped in very deep historical traditions.*

Soon after this brief conversation, Thomas fell asleep. Although he did not fall into a coma, he slept for several hours. When he woke up, they announced over the loudspeaker that they would be landing soon. Again, he first heard the soft, rhythmical sounds of Japanese followed by English with a strong Japanese accent. *We English speakers get catered to wherever we go.* Japanese sounded like a very steady beat to his ears. He heard the word "arigato": a-ri-ga-to. It had a very symmetric, rhythmical feel to it. He would later learn that this word means "thank you".

When they landed, it was a gray fall day outside. The sky was overcast. Japanese laborers in mini vehicles came up and efficiently unloaded the cargo coming off the plane. They looked very serious. It was inconceivable to imagine them acting out Abbott and Costello's "Who's on First."

He entered the airport. For a few minutes, he felt as if he were upside down on a roller coaster. *Where am I? Back in Paris, I imagined that I would lose homeostasis if I traveled to India. I seem also to have reached this mental state on my first day in Japan.*

He had seen some Japanese language writing in different areas of the plane, but now the Japanese alphabet was everywhere. In Europe, everywhere that he had gone used the Roman alphabet. Just this difference in the alphabet made him feel much more like a foreigner, or as he would learn later, a gaijin in Japan. Alphabets definitely set another boundary. It is saying to you: *if you have not learned our language, you have absolutely no idea what is written.* Often in French or Spanish, he could figure out what the word was, since it was close to English. For example, the words "bizarre" and "excellent" were the same in French, even though they were pronounced quite differently. There were many other words that were extremely similar, such as la bicyclette and populaire. It did not require extensive powers of deductive reasoning to figure out what these words meant. But there would be no such shortcut with Japanese. Possibly the same principles could apply once he learned the alphabet. Learning the alphabet, however, was an extensive additional process that was not required with the Roman alphabet languages.

Another aspect of his culture shock that smacked him in the face like a strong hurricane was that now he stood out racially in this land. He had never experienced being a racial minority before; he was used to blending in with the dominant culture as a white person. It was true that he was a minority as well on the plane ride, statistically speaking, but this was a small, contained group. Therefore, he did not feel the effect nearly as much. Now there were hordes of Japanese people walking around the airport, and all of the employees were Japanese as well. At most, five percent of the people in this facility were white (or some other race). In Europe, nobody immediately knew that he was a foreigner unless they spoke to him and heard his "Yank" accent. Now he could not hide from his "otherness" behind any corner or crevice. As soon as they saw him, they knew that he was a gaijin. He was not one of them. *It is going to take some time to become accustomed to this. I think that I really will be a talking monkey when I start teaching! They will be staring at me as if they were looking at a zoo animal through his cage. I merely need metaphorical bars around me in order for it to be equivalent. I am the "other" in a cage.*

It was a very different feeling, not blending in. Although Thomas had always felt like an outsider in Indiana psychologically, that was a quite distinct experience from feeling like an outsider based on his skin color or physical appearance. This was more of a "surface" type of outsider-ness, and because he was not used to it, it felt more awkward. He sometimes felt pride in being different from almost everyone in Indiana, but this feeling here in Japan was just discomfort. However, he thought that possibly he would become accustomed to being a minority with time. *Human beings are creatures of adjustment. We learn to adapt to different conditions. Would overseas travel be meaningful if no adjustments were required? Absolutely not!* Therefore, he preferred to view this as just another component of adapting to his new surroundings. After all, he had overcome the humiliation of ordering apple juice in a nice French restaurant. This could also be overcome.

He was waiting in a long line to clear Immigration. As he got closer to the front, he noticed a Japanese employee shouting

"Hai! Dozo!" The employee kept repeating this every ten seconds in a military-like fashion. He would later learn that "hai" meant yes and that "dozo" meant go ahead. In essence, the Japanese employee was saying "keep moving". At an American airport, they would not say this so formally and in such fixed intervals. Usually, an employee would just say "next" when needed. This behavior in the airport seemed to be another example of the Japanese formalism and, in his eyes, the tendency to exaggerate a phenomenon. Just as the woman on the plane could not just say "sorry" but had to say "soooooo sorry", this employee had to keep saying the equivalent of "next, please" with such extreme seriousness and as if it were part of a military drill. *Well, at least he is being consistent with the feeling of the Japanese language by keeping it at regular intervals. A-ri-ga-to, hai, do-zo.* He was aware of Japan's deeply militaristic history. It seemed to be the case that these military residues were continuing to permeate the society in unexpected ways. *I had never considered the possibility before that military culture would influence a procedure at the airport. But at the end of the day, culture is culture.*

After twenty minutes of waiting in line at the fairly busy Kansai International Airport, it was finally his turn to approach the immigration counter. A well-dressed Japanese woman who was approximately in her late twenties stood behind the window. She was wearing a fair amount of makeup, though it was microscopic compared to the amount that some of the ladies on the plane wore. *At least I can still see her basic features. This is definitely not a Kafka-like metamorphosis. Kafka would have found this case to be very uninspiring material.*

"Good morning," she said with a slight bow of the head.

"Good morning."

"Passport, please."

He handed it over.

"What is purpose of stay in Japan?"

"I will be teaching English."

"You have written offer from employer?"

"Yes."

He handed over his Gova employment offer. It was written in both Japanese and English or, as they appeared to Thomas, pictures and words. The Japanese alphabet appeared to be more picture-like in comparison. *Do they possibly use paint brushes when they write their essays in school? How do you erase painting though? White it out and paint over it? If a picture is worth a thousand words, then by this logic, we Westerners are much wordier with our alphabet. They are extremely concise and to the point in comparison. They certainly do not speak in that kind of manner though. Perhaps it can be flipped and I can argue that a Western interaction is worth a thousand Japanese interactions? One "next" equals a thousand "hai, dozo" intervals in terms of how frequently they occur?*

Thomas was scheduled for a week of training, followed by a one-year teaching contract. Therefore, his scheduled exit date (November 30, 2016) was in about a year. The lady stamped this date on his passport. She also stamped his entry date of November 23, 2015 and the seal of the port of entry (Kansai International Airport).

"Thank you," she said. Then as he exited the immigration terminal, he heard more shouts of "Hai, dozo!" *I missed you. I didn't hear it for thirty seconds while I waited for my passport to be processed, and that felt strange. This expression in this airport is similar to carbon dioxide. It's constantly being exhaled. If you don't hear it for thirty seconds, then it's the equivalent of someone who is having trouble breathing, gasping for air as they try to exhale their next batch of carbon dioxide. It's the man's pulse or heartbeat.*

Next, he had to pass through Customs. In this section, a thin man who was in his forties scanned Thomas's baggage with his eyes. He sucked in his lips a bit, and then began speaking.

"Do you have any alcohol?"

"No."

"Do you have any cigarette?"

"No."

"Do you have any perfume?" he asked in complete seriousness.

Thomas had to restrain himself from laughing.

"No."

Why would he think that I would have perfume? Do I appear to be some drama queen to him?

"Do you have...eto...toothpaste?"

"Yes."

Sorry to disappoint you there. It would be far preferable for me never to brush my teeth and blow lethal breath on you as you keep asking me all of these questions.

"Hmmm...how many toothpaste?"

"One tube."

Sorry, sir, I'm not a toothpaste bootlegger, though I'm sure that it would be a quite lucrative market to enter. I have watched many inspiring films of rival gangs killing each other over toothpaste territory. The dental lobby pushed to make toothpaste illegal at one point to increase their profits. Without toothpaste, the number of root canals done per day increased five hundred percent. Unfortunately, dating suffered terribly as well since it was difficult for people to become intimate when you could smell a person's breath from fifty feet away. The streets smelled similar to the days of the bubonic plague, where the stench of rotting bodies filled the air. The dental lobby decided that their increased profits from dental work were not worth having to endure the plague-like smells that were omnipresent on the streets. Just as Prohibition was overturned, history repeated itself, and toothpaste became legal again as well.

"Toothpaste not for sale?"

"No."

You're certainly welcome to buy it, though, if you're utterly curious what we gaijins use on our teeth. Judging by some of the teeth that I've seen so far in the airport, maybe I should sell my toothpaste to a worthy soul.

"Form, please."

Thomas handed him the customs form.

"Thank you."

Clearing Immigration and Customs was relatively low drama. It could have been far worse. *They did not run my bag through a machine, so they seem to be trusting that I'm following the regulations. Most likely, English teachers usually do not smuggle illegal goods into the country.*

After he cleared Customs, Thomas headed for the exits. He saw a Japanese man holding a sign with his name on it. *That must be me! It is extremely unlikely that there is another Thomas Gephardt in the Kansai airport today. If there were, I would definitely like to know his story though. Why did he come to Japan, and when the customs guy asked him if he had any toothpaste for sale, did he answer yes?* The man looked young with a beard. He was wearing a dress shirt and dress pants. *I have yet to see a sloppily dressed Japanese person. Where do all of the bums congregate? Where are the rebels who only say "sorry" instead of "soooooo sorry"? I will find out in due time.*

The Japanese man introduced himself as Hiroto Murasaki. "Come this way, please."

They exited the airport and went to the parking area. His car was a medium-sized green Toyota. *These do not look significantly different from the Toyotas that I've seen back home. It's good to know that we are driving authentic-looking Toyotas in the United States. Fake-looking Toyotas would be almost as unscrupulous as when art museums unintentionally display fake works of art. The Japanese probably see their car creations as works of art; therefore, I would not want a fake copy of one of these entities either.*

Hiroto opened the passenger door for him and bowed slightly. *This bowing is actually starting to feel somewhat normal. It seems less peculiar, the more that I witness the custom. The bow seems to imply more of a hierarchy present in the culture. Bowing to someone seems to imply that the other person is higher than you.*

A Western-style handshake, on the other hand, implies more equality since it is horizontal. He had previously read that the depth of the bow was directly related to the social status of the other person. A CEO, therefore, would receive a very deep bow as opposed to the very slight bow that Hiroto had given him. *Talking monkeys do not get deep bows; if we did, it would be rather absurd.*

"You share apartment with two people. You are close nice area Kyoto. Many nice restaurant and temple."

Thomas again noticed the lack of plurals in Japanese English. This tendency was not merely confined to Mr. Yamamoto at the London Gova office. Most likely, they did not have them in Japanese. He considered that, from a logical point of view, plurals are not absolutely necessary. *When he says, "many nice restaurant and temple", I completely understand what he is saying without any difficulties. The "many" is pretty much self-explanatory without pluralizing restaurant or temple. Plurals in English really are just a custom rather than a logical necessity. No plurals are the least of my worries. Most likely, they will be very much in the back of my mind when I become consumed with my daily life here.*

Hiroto drove at a reasonable speed, and he was not aggressive when changing lanes. He kept ample distance from the cars in front of him. It was like night and day compared to the drive home from the Bordeaux airport. *This definitely does not feel like a race car. Why is it that in some places, the drivers follow the rules, and in other places, they do not? Are Americans and the Japanese more "rule-oriented" generally than the French? In a country, is there a relationship between how the people drive and how much they follow other rules, such as tax rules and the rules of business?* He had also observed that the drivers in London seemed to be courteous as well, and England was known as a generally "clean" country in terms of corruption. *I have not done any empirical research, but my limited anecdotal experiences are definitely suggesting to me that the nature of driving in a country has some relationship to how much the rules are followed at a more wide-ranging level. Yes, how people drive tells me a lot about the country. These airport rides are an important first crash course (hopefully no pun intended) with regard to aspects of the country's culture.*

The ride to his apartment was very visually stimulating. In the beginning of the drive, he saw many restaurants, bars, and temples. Unfortunately, he could barely keep his eyes open after such a long plane ride. He mostly saw the darkness, a consequence of closed eyes. *There will be plenty of time later on for exploring. Right now, I need a good night's sleep after all of those hours flying across Europe and Asia.* Hiroto drove up to a modest-sized apartment building. He assisted Thomas with carrying up his bags. The building had an elevator, and the apartment was on the sixth floor.

"You share apartment. Two other teacher. They come later. Enjoy...eto...stay in Japan." He bowed slightly again with a medium-sized smile, and then left.

Thomas gave himself a tour of the apartment. *The photographer whom I imagined on the plane would need to zoom a lot, when he takes snapshots of the rooms and furniture. Mr. Yamamoto did warn me that living conditions would not be roomy. There are one hundred and twenty-five million people in Japan, in an area that is the size of California.* The kitchen had a small stove with an attached oven. The chairs in the family area were made out of bamboo wood, and the floor lamp had an interesting shape. It was shaped like a long, narrow cylinder. His room had a sliding door; he would later learn that this was called a shoji screen. *Well, I would never have an apartment that looks like this in Indiana. The only chance of seeing some of these objects in the United States would be in a museum.*

He chose a room, slid the shoji door open, and crashed on the bed. Several hours later, he woke up and heard voices (outside of his mind, thankfully). His other roommates had clearly arrived. They were sitting on the couch, watching television.

"How are you doing? I'm Thomas."

"Hey, man, I'm Albert."

Albert was very casually dressed, and he was about average height and weight. He had light brown hair and a quite chill demeanor.

"Hi Thomas, I'm Janek. Where are you from?"

Janek seemed to be more of a business type; he seemed to have much more of a corporate ethos. His countenance had a slight smirk. He was fairly tall and slender, and well dressed. He wore a nice-looking shirt with a collar and pants. He had dark hair. Thomas heard that they both had North American accents, so he replied, "Indiana. How about yourself?"

"I'm from Oregon. I studied in Japan during college, and I wanted to return to see a bit more of the country and possibly explore other opportunities for working here. What brings you to Japan?" Janek replied.

"I've recently become very interested in overseas travel. I spent a few months in France; I stayed with a family, studied the language, and worked in a hotel. I thought that the next logical step in my journey was to explore an Asian country, and teaching English seemed to be a good way to do this. I interviewed in London for this position. Albert, where are you from, and why did you decide to come teach here?"

"Japan has the most developed porn industry. You can walk down the street and buy porn magazines from a vending machine. How badass is that?"

Janek and Thomas both laughed.

"But anyways, I like to travel too. I'm originally from Houston, though I was living in Austin for a while right before coming over here," Albert added.

"Have either of you guys taught before?" he asked.

They both indicated that they had not; this was also their first teaching experience.

"That means that all three of us will be learning the ropes together. I've heard English teachers referred to as talking monkeys. Apparently, our training will teach us how to become one of these," Thomas said with a grin.

"I sure as hell feel like a freak here compared to back home, that's for sure. Back home, I'm a person. Here I feel like I'm being stared at all the time since I'm white," Albert said.

"You'll get used to the minority experience over time. That bothered me quite a bit during my first week or two, but after that, it wasn't so painful," Janek said.

"I hope so. I'll be in bad shape if I still constantly feel like a freak six months from now," Albert said.

"I'm more anxious about the teaching experience than just walking around the streets as a minority. I've never taught before, and I've never been particularly inclined towards public speaking," Thomas said.

"Just approach it as you should approach any job. Put in a lot of effort, and it should pan out well," Janek said.

Yes, Janek, you are definitely the corporate pleaser. I'm not sure if my heart is in this teaching endeavor yet; I was more focused on this as a means of travel rather than the teaching itself. Regardless, Thomas did agree that he should approach the activity with an open mind, thinking that if he soured on the whole teaching attempt too hastily, then it would affect his whole outlook here negatively. Although Thomas had some agreement with Janek's statement, he found Janek's aura to be just a bit too polished or slick. He definitely strongly preferred Albert's demeanor, who came across as much more natural. Albert didn't seem to have any special agenda; he just wanted to have a stimulating life experience in Japan. Janek seemed to have such an agenda already, as if he were plotting his networking strategy for advancing his career interests in Japan.

"Makes sense, Janek. Out of curiosity, what ethnicity is your name?"

"Czech. I was born in Prague, and my parents immigrated over to the United States when I was three."

"I see. My family has been in Indiana for a few generations, so I cannot claim any such close links with another land. We're all originally immigrants though, other than the Native Americans. Anyways, nice to meet you guys. I'm going to take a stroll around our neighborhood here."

Unaccompanied this time by Hiroto, he managed to find the floor buttons in the elevator. Thankfully, they were written in Arabic numerals. He would later learn that Arabic numerals were more common in horizontal writing; in vertical writing, Chinese numerals were preferred. Sauntering around his immediate surroundings, he could see that, just as in Europe, it was very crowded. The streets were smaller here, and shops were placed very closely together. He noticed that there were a lot of vending machines. It was difficult to walk more than a few minutes without seeing one; possibly that was one reason why Albert had referred to porn vending machines. If vending machines were so omnipresent, it was certainly conceivable that some of them might have porn, given Japan's reputation in this area. He walked up to one row of vending machines. Several forms of iced coffee were available, which he had never seen in a vending machine. Many fruit drinks or flavored water were available as well; he was not certain what these drinks were since he could not read Japanese. The machine next to it was filled with different frozen-food meals. *That is convenient if I need a quick meal. First, I will have to see how much I warm up to the food here.* The next machine had several different instant-noodle bowls of varying flavors. He would later learn that Japan has the most vending machines per capita of any country in the world.

He had envisioned loads of electronics here and he knew that there was an abundant sex industry. However, he was not expecting that it would be the world leader in vending machine frequency. *Possibly the abundance of vending machines is connected to the reserved nature of the Japanese? They would much rather buy something without interacting with a human cashier. Yes, vending machines are definitely a boon for shy, introverted people. They do deprive people of low-skill jobs economically, but they save the shy members of the human race from having to say hello and answer other questions. If I had gone to Japan before France, I would have liked to ask Paul if they had any vending machines in France that sold wine! It would have been very interesting to see his reaction. He might have possibly had a heart attack if I had asked that question, so possibly fate had it that I went to France first.* Vending machines selling wine would not happen in France, plain and simple. Most likely, the French would feel that the machine cheapened the quality and marketability of one of their proudest exports to the world. No, in France, you only buy wine from a caring professional. The professional counsels you, answers any questions, and hands it to you. France has never been known for being "tech-oriented" in the way that Japan is.

He continued walking through the streets. He stopped by an actual convenience store with a human clerk. He was beginning to get accustomed to seeing the Japanese alphabet everywhere, and then he noticed an alphabet that looked much more familiar. It was *The Japan Times*, an English-language newspaper. *Roman alphabet, how I have missed you.* He bought a copy of the paper along with some Japanese chocolate, and then he walked out.

Next door was a small clothing store. Two young Japanese girls, scantily dressed, stood outside. They wore very short skirts and the socks were pulled up quite high on their legs. They kept chanting some kind of greeting to the hordes of possible customers walking by. The constant repetition of this greeting brought back flashbacks of the "hai, dozo" man from the airport. *Apparently, some of these repetitive formalities are not merely confined to the airport. I do not know if I will ever be able to adapt to this aspect of Japan. It seems so phony to keep chanting the same greeting endlessly. A greeting needs to have some semblance of spontaneity, or it loses any kind of genuine meaning. Most likely to the Japanese people walking by, this is just a normal facet of their lives and it does not cause any additional thoughts.* He surmised that this was a key distinction between a native and a gaijin.

These observations seemed to be sufficient for his first stroll around the neighborhood. His eyes were still glazed over from the plane ride, and he still felt extremely self-conscious as a white person in a sea of Asians. *If I do ever get acclimated to this minority status, I'm going to write Janek a memo confirming his proposal. Then possibly we can have a three-course business lunch further discussing the growth possibilities of this proposition.* He was not completely against Janek though. He did seem to be an outgoing, lively guy and also mentally sharp. *I will probably have some stimulating discussions with him. The corporate persona will just require some adjusting after the mostly granola-type travelers that I met over in Europe. The Aussie guys back in France and even the Irish men in London were much more like Albert. They wanted to soak in their surroundings, but they did not seem to have any other agenda.* He headed back to the apartment. Janek and Albert were both chilling in their rooms. Since he was still extremely jet-lagged, he fell back asleep. He did not wake up again until the next day.

A few days later, he started his one-week training with the company. There were twenty teachers who were attending this training. The trainers were a mix of Japanese and native English-speaking employees. He learned that some of these gaijin had liked Japan enough to spend several years here and had moved into higher positions with the company. *That would be an interesting prospect to live in a foreign culture for several years. In France, I was only able to skim the surface of the culture due to the briefness of my stay. After several years, I doubt that I would ever feel like one of "them" in these countries, but I would have quite deep knowledge. It would be interesting to see how much, if any, my initial gut impressions changed over the years.*

A middle-aged woman named Jennifer was leading the training. She had blonde hair and was average weight, by Western standards. Compared to most of the Japanese people that Thomas had seen, she seemed a bit heavy. Since she was about average size for a Western woman, she also appeared to be quite large compared to the petite frames of most of the Japanese. *Yes, people are definitely much smaller here.* Jennifer was from Winnipeg.

"One of the most important aspects of our training will be teaching you about the educational style that Japanese students are used to. In their schools, they have very little opportunity to speak English. They mostly study grammar and vocabulary. Generally, in Asian classrooms, the teacher just lectures. There is very little Western-style discussion that most of you here are familiar with. In school or at your college, you may have had classes in which you debated different points of view. That is far less common here in Japan. The Japanese strongly emphasize group harmony. They are often very reluctant to express strong opinions because they are afraid that it might upset the balance of the group. The individual is emphasized far less here compared to our Western cultures."

Next, another trainer, named Richard, began to speak. He was from Manchester, England. He had a quite thick accent; it sounded quite different than the London accent that Thomas had heard for a few days when he was there. *The London accent sounds much more regal.* "Since they are not used to class discussion, engaging the students to speak English is no small task. It will require tenacity and stamina on your part to encourage your students to speak. Most students are afraid of making mistakes when they speak English. It's very important to be gentle and smile. Smiling will help begin to break down the barriers that your students are likely to feel with you. I really cannot emphasize enough how important this is. You may think that you are 'just a teacher' here, with visions of some of your teachers back home, but you will have much more success in developing a rapport with your students if you smile and seem friendly. I realize that this could be a challenge for some of you. Trust me; I'm not a natural smiler. I'm British," he said with a light laugh.

"It was work for me to have to smile this much, and it probably will be for some of you here. But it's part of your job, and as I've mentioned, it's extremely important. A lot of your students are going to be bloody petrified to put together English sentences. They want to learn to speak English; it's a global language and it helps a lot of them advance in their careers and travel to other places. For the Yanks who have joined us, try to teach them the proper Queen's English and not your bastardized American version," he said with a completely serious look on his face.

There's that dry, deadpan British humor. It does help lighten up the mood, though he might sincerely believe that their version of English is superior to ours. Often the original speakers of a language take that kind of view. It's as if they still see us as the colonized subjects with regard to our English. They, as the colonizer, need to teach us the "proper" way to speak English. American English is definitely much more casual, but that in and of itself does not make it inferior. I would argue that the fairest interpretation is that our version of the language is merely different, not bastardized.

Next, the trainers went over different methodologies to employ in the classroom. They showed different types of lessons in the textbooks that the teachers would be using. One type of lesson was a role-play for different types of situations. Another lesson taught vocabulary words that were associated with a certain topic (flying on a plane, for example) and then asked students to use the words in a sentence.

This is definitely not going to be an easy walk in the park, teaching here. *I am grateful for this opportunity to be exposed to Japanese culture, but I am going to be very tired from this kind of work. I'll be doing an enormous amount of talking with reticent students. Possibly I will feel jet-lagged every day. Every day will feel as if I've been on a long international plane ride. Well, it will make this into a more realistic life experience. When I just travel through a place, everything appears to be much shinier and "beachy" (in the case of the Spanish island). During this time, I will definitely not think that Japan is one endless night of debauchery, accompanied by geishas and porn machines. Nor will I think that life in Japan is reduced to sitting around, eating endless plates of sushi every day. No, this is not a fairy tale; I'm going to be coming home to my two American roomies, and I'll probably be completely knocked out from all of this talking to shy students. I have a hunch that I'll be earning every yen I get here.*

As training continued, they went over numerous different types of exercises that would be taught to the students. The main theme of the exercises was that they emphasized everyday, conversational life. *There won't be a lot of theoretical discussions in these classes. That makes sense; the students, by and large, aren't familiar enough with English to be able to have these kinds of conversations. Birthdays, sports, eating, drinking, and school will all be suitable topics. I will be evaluated on how well I can get the students to overcome their inhibitions and express thoughts on these ordinary facets of life.*

After a few days, Thomas began to tire of the training exercises. *At some point, I actually have to jump into the pool and swim. The only way to learn to teach is to actually do it. I mean, I never would have become comfortable with spicy food merely by reading a book about it or by participating in "simulations" of hot peppers inside my mouth.*

On his way home from training that day, he decided to try sushi for the first time. It was quite hard to find it in his hometown, and he had never had a strong craving in the past for raw fish. Psychologically, he found the idea of eating uncooked fish to be a bit repulsive. But there was also the countervailing fact that the Japanese lived extremely long lives. Therefore, how dangerous could raw fish be if it were prepared properly? He had also read that cooking fish often kills a lot of the healthy nutrients. From this perspective, it implied that it was even *wise* to eat the creature raw.

He saw a restaurant that had numerous photos of sushi on the outside. *Thank goodness for photos; otherwise how would we illiterate gaijin survive in this land?* It dawned on him for the first time that, with regard to the Japanese alphabet, he was quite literally illiterate. He was unable to read any of it. *It is indeed a very limiting condition to be illiterate. Most likely, only a limited part of the brain processes pictures alone. It's as if a huge chunk of my brain has been surgically removed and I only have access to the pictures or visual part. Fortunately, there is some English here. Words are important to me, even when I am out walking on the street, and I do not think that I can survive in a place where I cannot read anything. It simply feels too alienating.*

When he entered the restaurant, he was surprised to see that the sushi moved around on plates on a conveyor belt. He would later learn that such "sushi trains" were quite common in Japan. *So it is basically akin to a rotating buffet. Instead of walking over to a stationary buffet, the buffet comes to you and you choose which plates of raw fish that you would like to consume.* He thought that it was an interesting concept. Each plate of two pieces was roughly between two and three U.S. dollars. *This will get expensive quite rapidly if I have any appetite. No wonder that the Japanese are so thin! They would bankrupt themselves if they ate large quantities of this food.*

A tall man with a white chef's hat was busy chopping up the raw fish and placing it on the rice in the center of the train area. *If I spoke enough Japanese, I would ask our culinary conductor if there is an extra-large value meal option. Surely the influence of McDonald's has splashed over to sushi trains? Unfortunately, unlike in the famous Beatles song, I do not think that I have a ticket to ride on this one. Most likely, I would receive the equivalent of a rejection followed by a bow. Even though my question is unbelievably foolish, it is conceivable that the chef would still bow in respect. What he might be pondering on the inside in response to my question (assuming that he comprehended it) is an entirely different, opaque matter. I never know what they are thinking; it is all hidden behind a veneer of surface politeness and formality. I feel as though I am in a constant mode of guessing and uncertainty here. Every interaction feels like a riddle or puzzle. This might seem exciting for a few days, but will I still feel the same after a year (or month) of teaching and daily life? I have my doubts about that. If I am capable of surviving a year in this mysterious land, I must learn to be very patient. Straightforward Western interactions are anything but de rigueur. This will be a character test; can I be open minded enough not to get frustrated by the indirectness of the culture? Only time will tell the answer to that inquiry. In that respect, I have a hunch that this will be a significantly more challenging experience than France. Unquestionably, there were cultural differences that I had to deal with over there, but I did not feel that I was on a completely different plane (or galaxy) than the natives. No, the French and Americans have descended from more common cultural origins; hence, the differences did not feel as stark. In the book that I browsed about Japan, it said that Japan is quite culturally different even from the other Asian countries. Japan is not merely physically an island. It is very much culturally and socially one as well. They follow their own rules and walk along a quite distinct path from the rest of us.*

The expression "when in Rome..." definitely applies here; I can tell that I am expected to adapt to their ways, which is as it should be. They make no apologies for departing from the Western path. Although they seem to be quite reserved, I do detect a mild pride in their cultural customs. I cannot fault them for having some pride in a unique culture that has developed out of centuries of tradition. Uniqueness is not always meritorious in and of itself, but there is something viscerally "cool" about sushi trains, samurai warriors, neon signs in the streets, and vending machines that offer everything imaginable. They are a successful country economically; we Americans are proud of our success, and they certainly have the same right to claim respect at the table of nations.

He realized that, in many respects, it was humbling to be living in the country that had the second or third largest economy. The United States was the only superpower at this time, but it was not the only powerful country from an economic point of view. Thomas could "feel" the economic power of Japan in the clean, nice-looking buildings and in the well-designed airport. *Yet this power was developed from a completely dissimilar set of customs and cultural beliefs. It refutes the views of some back home that the American way is the only way to success.*

Returning back to physical reality (which often was far less gratifying than the ponderings of his inner mind), he took a seat and grabbed a menu. He mainly grabbed the menu out of curiosity about its contents; he knew that he was going to order from the "rotating buffet". *If only they had train music to accompany the plates of sushi: "I think I can, I think I can, I think I can." Yes, plate of raw fish, you can do it; you can move along to that hungry "salaryman" over there before he meticulously takes his chop sticks, puts you in his mouth, and ends your existence. I'm sure that you had a great life before a fisherman murdered you in cold blood. At least you died for a good cause; sushi is one of the world's great delicacies. Your nutrients and omega–3 content help sustain and extend human lives; this additional information should make you feel infinitely better about your premature death. Your death helps us live longer; thank you for your heroic sacrifice!*

After a few minutes, he was given a bowl of soup. Later he would learn that this was called miso soup. It was much less chunky than the soups that he was used to; it was primarily liquid, with a yellow color. Its flavor was relatively mild. *My mouth is quite dry after eating the soup. It was very salty. How long did it take to mine this amount of salt? I need a few glasses of water to return to normal. I am not usually this dehydrated in November!* Overall, he felt pretty neutral about it; it seemed useful for warming up in cold weather and the flavor wasn't terrible, but it was not a particularly delicious soup either. Again, he had to repress those memories of delicious French cooking.

He first picked up a plate of two pieces of raw salmon. The thought of eating raw food for the first time made his stomach queasy; now, he had an "abnormal" stomach to go along with his still-somewhat-dry throat. For a minute, he had nagging doubts about his decision to try this delicacy. *I have to follow through; I call myself an adventurous wanderer.* He took one piece, closed his eyes, and swallowed.

It has a quite rich flavor! Perhaps cooked food is not always necessarily superior. The green wasabi sauce that was in between the raw fish and the rice made it quite spicy. The general experience of travel was making him more open to different kinds of food, and therefore, he didn't mind the increased spiciness from the wasabi. *As with everything else in my travels, it is a new experience, and toleration for spice can be built up over time. If all of these other Japanese people can "handle" the wasabi, what makes me as a gaijin so radically different that I cannot eat it? Yes, my skin is lighter than their skin is, and my facial features are different. I am larger, on average, than most of them, but we are all essentially part of the same human race, or at least I hope so. True, most likely, I will always feel like a gaijin here, even if I lived here for ten years. I am not them, and I don't think that I could ever learn to communicate in such a subtle manner. But when it comes to physical consumption of food, it shouldn't be that foreboding to get used to wasabi. I am willing to wager that after three or four times eating sushi, it will feel like an old habit. However, I do understand more now why the miso soup is served with the sushi. It helps calm down the mouth after eating the wasabi, even if the soup itself is not extremely flavorful.*

He tried three other plates: tuna, mackerel, and squid. The salmon and tuna were his favorites. He felt pretty neutral about the other two. Nevertheless, he thought that this meal was a major milestone and showed his continued growth as an expatriate. *I have now eaten raw food and I am building up my tolerance for spice. Whom do I know back in Indiana who eats sushi or wasabi? Travel makes it so much easier to try new foods. Back home, it would have seemed simply too terrifying or strange to eat sushi, even if it were available. But here in Japan, on the other hand, it's difficult to avoid sushi. It is as omnipresent here as water. It's challenging to walk through a subway or train station without passing by sights of the food. Yes, to spend time in Japan and never eat sushi would be similar to never eating pizza in Italy or never eating a baguette in France. If someone spends at least a month in Japan and they never try sushi, then they deserve a royal "WHAT THE HELL IS WRONG WITH YOU?" as a response. This is indeed an island that is by definition surrounded by water. It makes perfect logical sense that they would have developed this kind of cuisine. Yes, the long-term globetrotter who insists on avoiding sushi should take a long swim in the waters with the fish (that are not yet sushi) and think twice about returning to Japan. Swim over to another land where it isn't such an integral part of their customs and diet.*

With his new pride established about adapting to his new home and his mouth still on fire from the wasabi, he walked back to the train station. On the ride back to his apartment, he was engrossed in a *Japan Times* article about some turmoil in the European Union over funding for anti-terrorism efforts. As he was about to scan for other articles to read, he noticed something out of the corner of his eye. He looked up, and a group of older ladies had a firm gaze on him. They quickly looked away after he began to stare back.

Well, I am a talking monkey. Here I am, on display, in my cage, on the subway. If you were going to stare at me, couldn't you at least have thrown a banana my way? I give you my apologies for the gaijin invasion. Now if only I could be conditioned to do that uber-polite bow. I would most certainly bow if I had received a delicious organic banana. If it had been an inorganic one, then I probably would have responded with a milder bow. We talking monkeys need our organic nutrients just as much as you humans do.

A few days later, he began teaching. He found his classroom with little difficulty. However, he hesitated for a minute, walked around the corner, and then reluctantly headed back to the room. In many respects, this felt more fear-provoking than the initial flight to France. He felt that there was more on the line now. He had a job and there were expectations that he needed to engage his students. On the flight to France, the future was brimming with intriguing possibilities. However, this did not accurately describe his state of mind today. He was unsure about how much passion he really had for teaching. He was primarily doing this job to experience Japan, not teaching. *Well, hyperventilating about the first day will get me nowhere. It's time to jump into the pool with some minimal confidence. What would be the equivalent of "drowning" on the first day? Based on my observations so far, they're not going to boo me out of class. They seem to be far too polite for that. The worst-case scenario seems to be if we just stare at each other or the ground for the entire class and I completely fail to stimulate any dialogue. That is somewhat probable.* These optimistic thoughts were swirling around his head as he entered his classroom, wearing a shirt, tie, and dress pants.

He had noticed in the morning that he had not tied his tie as flawlessly as Janek. Janek's tie looked smooth, pristine, and perfectly lined up on his shirt. Thomas, being far less experienced with ties, struggled to find the right length. After about twenty minutes of trying, he settled for "good enough". *It's above my scrotum and below my man-boobs. That is the essence of "good enough" with these garments that they misleadingly call ties; they should be called a choke cloth based on how they make me feel.*

Soon, his students entered. None of them were late. *They seem to keep time well here.* His classroom was a mix of three men and two women. He first asked the students to introduce themselves, as common logic would entail. The three men were Genjiro, Ichiro, and Masato. The two women were Hiroko and Maiko. Genjiro was a middle-aged "salaryman", as they were commonly called in Japan. He wore a suit to class. Masato was a university student at Doshisha University; he had decided to skip the suit in favor of some hip-looking jeans. Thomas was elated to see someone dressed a bit less formally. *Thank two hundred geishas (or sumo wrestlers) that he has the freedom and adventure during college to ditch the suit! No choke cloths for college students; humans have to experience some freedom and elasticity at some point in life.* He thought that wearing choke cloths for the entirety of a human life was a fate worse than death.

Ichiro was an older man who had recently retired from the workforce. He did not wear a suit, but he was not wearing hip jeans specially marketed to senior citizens, either. He wore a dress shirt and immaculately pressed black slacks. Hiroko was also a university student at Doshisha University. Maiko was a housewife; she appeared to be in her late twenties, though he found it more difficult to guess the ages of the Japanese compared to Westerners. The women, especially, seemed to age less quickly compared to Western women. He would later learn that Maiko was actually in her late thirties and she merely looked ten years younger. He didn't have to speculate about the ages of the university students. Once they indicated that they were college students, he then knew roughly the broader parameters of their possible ages. This "aid" was another piece of evidence that the Japanese looked younger than their Western counterparts; if Thomas had been required to guess the ages of Hiroko and Masato, he would have thought that they were high school students. Masato looked like a high school senior partly because of his facial scruff. Hiroko, on the other hand, easily could have fooled him that she was sixteen.

"Thanks, everyone, for the introductions. What are your hobbies?"

Now there was the petrified silence that the trainers had told him that he should expect in his classroom. Nobody volunteered to speak.

"Does everyone understand what I mean by 'hobby'?"

Again, there was stone-cold silence. *Cold Stone Creamery ice cream is just a name back home; here it's literally stone cold, much colder than any possible combination of ice cream flavors. Are they afraid to admit that they don't understand what I mean? Or are they afraid to speak English in general, other than saying, "My name is X and I am a student/office worker, etc."?* Upon reflection, it did seem to involve more thought to talk about a hobby rather than merely stating their names and occupations or stages of life. *Okay, I'm going to have to call on one of them in a non-military style; the "hai, dozo" approach is unlikely to stimulate lively conversations. No, that will probably make the atmosphere change from stone cold to stone hypothermia in here.*

Let's start with Genjiro, the "salaryman", as they call these types here. Possibly he will be more motivated since one would think that he is learning English for work-related purposes.

"Genjiro, do you understand my question about hobbies?"

"Eto...hobby is job?"

"No. Hobbies are activities that we do for fun. We do these by choice because we enjoy them. Do you have a hobby?"

He smiled bashfully, and looked down at the ground before returning to a normal posture and responding.

"No time to do hobby. Many hour with company. Weekend, sleep."

Thomas was not quite expecting that extreme of an answer. *Damn, that sounds like a completely soulless existence. He works and sleeps. Based on his description, that certainly sounds like a deep departure from* Dead Poets Society's *sucking all the marrow out of life. Genjiro's routine is much more analogous to the leftover chicken bones that are thrown in the dumpster; his existence has no marrow whatsoever.* He could see Mr. Keating saying, "Gentlemen, do you want to be a bone full of succulent, life-enhancing marrow, or do you want to be just a dull, pure skeleton-like bone?" *It is possible to subsist as a skeleton with minimal physical bones, but where is the humanity? No matter how much you paid me, I could not tolerate that kind of existence. No amount of money can justify a marrow-less reality.*

"Thank you, Genjiro."

"Maiko, do you have a hobby?"

Maiko first responded with an open-teeth smile. *They do smile here a lot more than the people did in France; that seems to be indisputable. Here, I don't feel yet that they are big smilers, but it certainly seems to be a more "normal" part of interactions compared to France. It seems to go well with this group harmony that they claim to value very much. Can you have a harmonious group feeling if nobody is smiling or laughing? It certainly seems that this goal would be harder to accomplish. Yes, this is a good thing that Maiko is smiling; it is a sign that she is at least trying to converse with me in a different language.*

Smiles, if they are genuine, do promote cooperation and harmony. Can I be one hundred percent sure that Maiko's smile is genuine, based on my initial feelings about the formality and decorum here? No. But regardless, I must, as a decent human being, give her the benefit of the doubt. Who wants to teach a classroom full of scowling students? Maiko is endeavoring to make the classroom environment more congenial; only a fool would argue that this action is not laudable.

Maiko replied, "Don't know how say in English. One moment."

She browsed through her dictionary and then said, "Gardening."

Okay, that is a legitimate hobby. It is somewhat of a "stereotypical" hobby that I would expect from a housewife, but it is certainly a hobby that nurtures the soul for some individuals. I do not enjoy being near dirt and soil, but I can see how it would be satisfying to grow your own plants. Regardless, it is a much more satisfying response compared to Genjiro's. Returning to Mr. Keating, he would probably respond to this statement by naming a famous poet who wrote deep lines about plants and nature, such as Whitman's "Leaves of Grass". This does seem to be hard work, teaching these students. It is a quite different experience than the thought-provoking conversations that I had with Paul. Since they are beginning-level students, I ask questions, and if I am lucky, I get a one-word answer. Can I do this for several hours a day? I may need the endurance level of an Olympian if every class is similar to this one. Now it is time to push on, with strength, to the next lap of these rough waters; I will ask the next student the same question. I will ask Hiroko to pontificate in one word or less about her hobbies; apparently in this classroom, answering with more than three words would be a filibuster.

"Hiroko, what are your hobbies? Do you also spend your free time gardening?"

He wanted to ask her if she planted wild animals, hoping to see them rise above ground as a reincarnated, different species. However, he knew that there was zero chance of her understanding him, much less getting the humor. *Teaching English to basic-level speakers is probably not the ideal profession for mouthing off my wit. Perhaps I would have a better chance of using my wit if I taught American English to Brits, if any of them desired to learn our version of the language. It seems to be the case that they are quite at ease with biting irony, if the Monty Python films are a true representation of the culture. Yes, the wild animals in the garden comment would probably play much better with them than in this classroom.*

In this classroom, the students were not comfortable speaking English. Therefore, he needed to keep the conversations relatively simple, and he needed to refrain from being a smart aleck.

He thought that in order to build rapport with these students, because of the formality of Japanese culture, he needed to be the opposite of a smart aleck. He needed to be a courteous gentleman. This kind of behavior felt very stilted to him, based on his desire to constantly infuse ironic moods into conversations. However, he considered that, possibly, it would be a character-building experience to learn to behave like a gentleman, at least for one year. *Surely a person is capable of a wide range of behavior merely for a year? Yes, I can learn to be an actor here. It's not a life sentence; I should just think of it as a one-year "service project". Ten or fifteen years from now, I will look back on this service project as I should look at other volunteer work: it was an uncomfortable task that forced me to grow and see this world from a different angle.*

Hiroko was about to respond to him, but she began to blush. She looked like she was about to giggle, and then covered her mouth. He would later learn that this was common behavior for Japanese women; it wasn't considered "ladylike" for them to laugh in public. Therefore, when they had the impulse to laugh, they would cover their mouths. He thought that laughing for Japanese women seemed equivalent to sneezing for Westerners. Openly sneezing in public was also considered to be improper in the West. Once again, if witty comments worked well here, he could ask her next time if she needed a tissue for her laughing. *Blow out your guffaws into the tissue; it will teach you not to do something so unhealthy like laugh next time!* Apparently for Japanese women, laughter was seen as the worst medicine, not the best. *Don't sit near Hiroko; she has a terrible disease! She likes to laugh. If you don't watch out, it could be contagious, and you might wind up laughing too! How horrific! Quarantine the gigglers, chucklers, and cacklers and anyone else who looks as though they're about to put on an expression of merriment.*

After Hiroko took her hand away from her mouth, she said, "I like shopping."

This was part of the "script" that he was expecting; shopping was another "stereotypical" hobby for a young woman. He knew that Japan was often associated with consumerism. When he rode home from the airport, he did see the outlines of a smaller shopping district in Osaka. He later read that Tokyo had a district called Ginza, which was extremely famous for shopping. *Okay, let's do a follow-up question for Hiroko.*

"Are you a general shopper, Hiroko, or are there certain goods or things that you like to buy?"

She indicated that she liked to shop for many things. She mentioned cosmetics, clothes, video games, and books. He was happy to hear that she had diverse interests; he did not want all of his students to be caricatures of common stereotypes. He had felt that he was headed for a crash landing in this area up to this point in the classroom. So far, he had "interviewed" an overworked company man, a housewife who liked gardening, and a student who was into shopping, but it was not only for strictly materialistic types of items.

"Do you read Japanese authors or authors from other places?"

"Last year, I read Harry Potter. In school, I read Japanese author."

"Do you ever read Japanese authors for your own pleasure?"

"Not so much. But maybe in future I do."

Harry Potter was a very global phenomenon, so he was not the least bit surprised that a younger student would have been interested in these books. Thomas had never been particularly interested in the Harry Potter series, but it did seem to be a story that would excite all corners of humanity. All children could connect with wizards, flying brooms, and other such phenomena.

He wondered if any of the ideas of Harry Potter would get lost in translation in the Japanese version. Unfortunately, there was no means of pondering this question without being fluent in Japanese.

He had read an interview a few years ago with the famous Jewish writer Isaac Bashevis Singer. Singer originally wrote in Yiddish, the historical language of Eastern European Jews. Singer said in the interview that he read the English translations of his works to see if they remained faithful to the original version, but he had no idea what happened to his novels in Japanese. Thomas thought for a few moments about that statement. *That would bother me a bit if I could not "audit" my works that had been translated into a foreign language. How would I know that they had not completely distorted the meaning of my ideas and the flow of the story when they translated the book? Unless I knew all of the world's languages fluently, I would have to merely settle for faith in the competence and good intentions of the translator. If the translator had a good reputation and solid credentials, then this could assuage some of the anxiety. This really was no different than "trusting" scientists with regard to their numerous theories. I do not know quantum physics or molecular biology in detail. Sure, I can read a summary of the ideas of the theory in the textbook, but I cannot independently verify the validity of the theories. I also have to trust the competence of the scientists.*

Now it was time to ferret out some words of wisdom from Ichiro, the most "seasoned" member of the group. Returning to his sardonic mind, he considered that if Ichiro would just become very fat, then he could make claims to be an elder, wise Buddha. Surely much of the appeal of Buddha was that his wisdom was contained in all those layers of fat of his belly? *Yes, wisdom is from the belly, not the brain. Those of us who are thin lack wisdom and therefore are heavy on foolishness. How can I communicate to Ichiro that I want him to start eating a lot more burgers and less seaweed and vegetables? Again, between the language barrier and the absurdity of this potential comment, this exchange also sounds like a Titanic-sized train wreck. A Titanic-sized train wreck in Japan would be two bullet trains (or shinkansen as they are called here) crashing into each other at 150 miles per hour. Most of my "conversation proposals" that keep flowing through my twisted mind are akin to bullet train crashes in physical reality. I am a fish out of water in this place. Fish on land trigger bullet-sized train crashes.*

"Ichiro, what are your hobbies?"

He did not appear to be as terrified to answer as the other students. On the other hand, since he was now the fourth student that was asked this question, he had also been given plenty of time to ponder what response he would give.

"Fish in boat and I like Sake."

Thomas googled this term on his phone. Sake was Japanese rice wine. Here he was, back to discussing wine. He thought that he had escaped the omnipresence of this topic after he departed France. But no, the ghost of French wine had now been reincarnated as Sake. *I can only wonder what Paul would think about Sake. Would he write it off as inferior to French wine? Or would he recognize it as a legitimate member of the wine family? I wish that I could call Paul right now; he would be thrilled to learn that the wine bottle had returned to daily conversations.* He could imagine Paul saying, "Try your apple juice smart-ass comments over there and see how many samurai warriors come running after you! You will be a dead man faster than you can say kamikaze!"

"How much Sake do you drink, Ichiro?"

"One bottle, every day."

That is quite a bit of alcohol consumption. No, I am not going to call him out as an alcoholic in front of his peers in this class. That would be especially cruel on the first day of class, and not gentlemanly manners on the two-hundredth day of class either. Yet, somehow, he has survived to his old age on these drinking habits. One of those Buddhas out there is looking out for him, even if he hasn't grown a Buddha belly from all of this imbibing. What does he eat to stay so fit? Furthermore, he must have a quite high tolerance if he drinks that much wine while fishing. Surely, otherwise, it would impair his concentration, if he intends to catch any fish. It is also possible that he merely finds it relaxing to sit in the boat out in the water since he has a lot of free time. Perhaps he fishes more for the relaxation; he does not have a significant desire to catch copious amounts of fish.

"Do you catch many fish?"

"No. Many fish already gone from water. I like nature. Wine is nice...eto...when see nature," he said with a slight nod of his head.

"Okay. In the last year, how many fish did you catch?"

"Hmmm...Ten, twenty fish."

Alright, so he does catch some fish. He isn't futilely sitting out on his boat, only getting inebriated on Sake. But it sounds like a casual fishing habit; he is more focused on enjoying the outdoors and his alcohol. That is not necessarily a regrettable habit during retirement. Thomas could think of many other ways to spend the day during retirement that were far worse.

Now it was time for the final stop on this Middle Earth plane of hobbies. Surely now he would find the one hobby ring to unite them all in this classroom. Nobody wanted a tragic ending on the first day of English immersion.

"Masato, we have an expression in English that is called 'last but not least'. It means that although you are the last person to be asked this question, you are just as important as the other students in the class. What are your hobbies?"

"Hobby...pachinko."

Pachinko: Thomas had read about this game before he arrived in Japan. He had also seen a pachinko parlor when he was walking around the streets of Kyoto. This was a quite popular pastime in Japan. It was a Japanese arcade game, more or less. Again, this seemed to be somewhat stereotypical of a young Japanese male; the stereotype was that they were heavily into gaming.

"Why do you like pachinko, Masato?"

His expression remained quite subdued and distant. "Fun. Tired to study book. Much school study. Enough study."

Yes, pachinko does seem to be a release from the stresses of everyday Japanese life. They have to conduct themselves so politely all the time; if I had that albatross hanging over me day and night, I could see the strong allure of a relatively mindless game such as pachinko. He thought back to the famous song by Queen where Freddie Mercury sang about "wanting to break free". It is not necessary to be proper when playing pachinko. It seems to serve a similar purpose as yoga for some, in the respect that it liberated people temporarily from societal pressures. He thought of Newton's law that for every action, there is an equal and opposite reaction. Surely in such a polite, formal society, there would be some kind of "reaction"? Pachinko seemed to be a subset of this reaction. In that sense, Pachinko was helping Japanese society to stay in equilibrium and prevent more negative consequences of too much inner repression, such as suicide and severe depression.

Thomas concluded the lesson by giving them a sheet of sentences to help them describe themselves with blanks. For example, one sentence would say "I often feel _____". Another would say, "My best birthday was when I _____". This was an easier activity since it required just thinking of one or two words, rather than asking an open-ended question. Open-ended questions seemed to be difficult with this class of students. He recalled again the comment from Jennifer during the training that there were very few Western-style discussions in the Japanese education system. Now he had observed this fact himself. It certainly was not a controversial question to ask students their hobbies. Yes, they were taking a course in another language, which would explain some of the nervousness. But they seemed quite afraid to speak at all, even about something as tame as hobbies. Yes, those philosophical, freewheeling, café-style settings that he observed in France did not seem to fit the landscape particularly well here. There were conversations, to be sure, but generally of the milder kind and generally keeping with the strict decorum of the culture. Once again, he was very grateful to be traveling around the world in order to observe a variety of cultural arrangements.

He taught five more lessons that day. Some of the classes had students who were at a slightly higher level of English; they knew more vocabulary words and could express slightly more complex ideas in sentences. But none of the classes were particularly loquacious; he had to push, pull, and yank quite hard to stimulate conversation. *I should have just been a dentist if I were going to pull teeth all day; that would have been far more lucrative. Each tooth that I yank out here to speak English generates about the equivalent of one small skewered piece of chicken on a stick.* (Several pieces on one stick were known as yakitori; it was one example of street food in Japan.) *I am absorbing a rich and varied cultural experience, but it is very obvious after today that this is not an extended vacation. This is not analogous to lying on the beach in Majorca; this is grueling toil. Perhaps, after one year, I will need to be carried back on a stretcher to Indiana from "verbal hypothermia". This job is unquestionably a very talkative one. Since I am used to being more of a quiet thinker, this is quite a shift. If I need to get surgery to replace my worn-out vocal cords, then I will know that it is time to hang it up as an English teacher and find another means of earning money. Short of this extreme outcome, I believe that I will be able to endure this year of teaching and marathon talking sessions with taciturn students.*

When Thomas returned to his apartment, Albert was sitting in a relaxed posture on the couch, browsing through a comic book. Janek was in his room, engaged in a phone conversation. *It sounds like he's already wheeling and dealing. He doesn't waste a precious moment. I was certainly placed with two contrasting roommates; just as world cultures have tremendous deviations from each other, so do the people within my own culture. Admittedly, the United States is an immigrant country; there will be a myriad number of cultural influences and combinations within the society.*

If he had traveled widely in the United States, wouldn't this be wide exposure as well? Yes, in a sense. There was certainly much variation in the cultural landscape of the U.S. compared to his sheltered small town. But these differences were still anchored by some kind of American nucleus. Following a blender analogy, there were many different cultures that were thrown into the blender, but they were ground up into some kind of amorphous American mix. British culture seemed to be the strongest influence with regard to the laws, legal system, and business practices. (Britain would be the equivalent of the water and ice in the blender.) However, Thomas could certainly feel strong differences from the British people whom he had met in England compared to his native compatriots. Royalty had been cast aside in the United States, and the style of English was much more casual and less "proper".

"How was your first day of teaching, Albert?"

"Man, I am completely wiped from this shit. I thought teaching was going to be easy. This is a j-o-b. That's one reason why I'm browsing through this Japanese comic. I need to convince myself that I'm doing something over here!"

"I hear you. I'm completely exhausted as well, or knackered, as some of my British acquaintances would say. I really like that word; it captures the essence of the physical state much better than the term 'exhausted.' But I digress. It is hard work teaching these students."

"Hell yeah! If I didn't have some hot female students in my classes, I'm on the plane back to Austin tomorrow. Sayonara, Japan, nice to meet you," he said with a very large grin, laughing into his comic book.

"Hmmm...I can't say that I have any students like that. I think the owner of the school steered those students towards you. Perhaps they picked up that aspect of your character during the training. They saw the porn magazines hidden in your training materials," Thomas said with an even larger smirk.

Albert laughed in response. "I do know enough to separate work from porn. You have to have a work-porn balance; that is very important."

Thomas liked that term: work-porn balance. *I'm fortunate to have been matched up with one entertaining roommate. This will lessen the difficulty of this one-year journey if I know that I have a humorous companion at my apartment.*

"Do you understand the story of the comic if you can't read Japanese?"

"You just have to use your imagination, Thomas. It's a good exercise in scrutinizing visual information."

"That's a good way of looking at it. As they say in the Taco Bell commercial: 'think outside the bun', right?"

"Be my guest if you want to think of it that way. In Texas, Taco Bell is such garbage compared to the real Mexican food that we eat."

Thomas thought this made sense. Since Texas was so proximate to Mexico, the abundance and quality of the Mexican food must be far superior to Taco Bell's generic, Americanized version. Returning to the blender analogy, Taco Bell's version was akin to putting a huge amount of water into the blender, watering down the quality of the other authentic Mexican ingredients. *I will go to Texas someday*, he decided. *After I've sojourned through the deserts of Africa and the unpaved streets of Afghanistan, then I will experience this more authentic Mexican food that they have in Texas. In the river of global travel, the main course comes first, and then the easy dessert comes later.*

For dinner that evening, Thomas decided to be mildly adventurous and cook a meal. His cooking experience was limited; in the past, he had been able to rely on the meals from the university cafeteria and later in France from Marie. He did have deep enough culinary knowledge to sauté chicken. He had seen teriyaki dishes in several Japanese "fast casual" type places that were near his apartment. He also knew that Japan was known for this seasoning; the word sounded Japanese, after all. It had the symmetry that was common to so many Japanese words: consonant, vowel, consonant, vowel, consonant, vowel. Te-ri-ya-ki. This symmetry was what gave the Japanese language its distinct rhythm. The large presence of vowels made the language sound softer compared to German or the Russian that he had heard on the streets of London. He had learned from another teacher that the Japanese were unable to pronounce "McDonald's" because the ending had too many consonants in a row. Therefore, they had made a Japanese adaptation to the word and called it "McDonaldo". He thought that McDonaldo sounded slightly more elegant than McDonald's. *Thus, when I experience the customary cardiac arrest after a meal there and feel the acute chest pains from the enchanting vitamins and antioxidants in the food, at least I can be reassured that the place had an elegant-sounding name. That should provide some psychological sustenance to help deal with the feeling of near death after McDonald's meals; no wonder that the Japanese live so much longer than Americans! They gave fast food places better sounding names to help their mental well-being.*

However, he had struggled to find teriyaki sauce in any of the food markets around his neighborhood. Because of the language barrier, he partly relied on the appearance of the sundry sauces in the aisles, but nothing seemed to resemble teriyaki. After searching for the condiment at three or four different places, he threw in the towel and decided to ask his parents to send him a bottle. His mother had been kind enough to send a bottle by express mail.

Janek had now entered the common area. Thomas mentioned this sequence of events to both of them and showed Albert the bottle. Albert laughed heartily. "This says made in Japan," he said.

Janek added, "Your bottle started in Japan, was shipped over to the U.S., and then came back to Japan. Very efficient."

"True, I should have just asked the Japanese plant to hold a spare one for me. I would have had to figure out how to explain to them that I was completely incapable of finding this sauce in a supermarket. Though, of course, they're so polite here; they would probably just nod their head, smile, and reserve the sauce. Or they would provide some convoluted explanation why it isn't possible to keep one for me. The convoluted explanations seem to help both parties save face," Thomas noted.

"Yes, you have picked up that aspect of Japanese culture rather quickly. Saving face is *everything* in Japan. If you don't save face, it's equivalent to social suicide. It took me longer to grasp that characteristic of life here; congratulations on picking this up already," Janek said.

"Thanks, Janek, I do my best to be observant. However, when it comes to schmoozing and networking, I cannot hold a candle to you. You have probably made more contacts since the beginning of our training than I will make during my entire time in Japan."

Janek slightly lowered his eyes. He then replied calmly with a stoic and neutral countenance, "We all have our different talents and foibles."

Thomas felt vibes from Janek that he didn't want super intense conversations. He seemed to mostly desire brief exchanges and keeping smooth relations with his roommates. *He seems to be the diplomat and deal maker, even in his worst nightmares. Albert puts up far fewer walls. He is the real deal: the meat in the sandwich, so to speak. Janek is the shiny coating on a piece of pottery that only shines temporarily. Nonetheless, humanity would be quite vapid if we were all uniform. I claim to prize the diversity of human expression; surely, I can work to find virtues in Janek's social interactions. He did compliment me, after all, on my perceptiveness.*

Thomas took back the bottle and prepared his dinner. He made teriyaki chicken with rice. It was quite a contrast to the complexity of Marie's elaborately prepared meals. However, he thought that it was a respectable effort from a culinary neophyte. *Teriyaki bottle, your journey across the Pacific twice for this meal was worth every mile. You probably weathered several different types of conditions before arriving at this table. Know that your expedition was not in vain. This tormented soul feels highly indebted for the distinct flavor that your expedition made possible. Rest in peace, portion of the teriyaki bottle that I just used.*

In addition to teaching, the teachers in this program also from time to time organized social outings. They mostly socialized among themselves since they had much more in common with each other compared to the Japanese natives; the language and cultural barriers were much smaller. A couple of weeks later, one teacher organized an outing to "Japanese-style" karaoke. Thomas had not researched what this term meant. Janek, of course, knew all of the minutiae of this custom.

"How is Japanese-style karaoke different from karaoke back in the United States?" he asked Janek at the apartment while he was eating a delicious tuna sandwich; the canned tuna in Japan tasted much fresher than American canned tuna. Unlike his teriyaki bottle, this tuna most likely had stayed in Japan and had not had the joy of two sojourns across the Pacific.

"Japanese style is in a private room instead of the public bar. You don't have to sing in front of strangers, and it's *a lot more* expensive. You are charged an hourly fee for use of the room in addition to any food and drinks that you order. You would have to really imbibe heavily in an American bar for it to be as expensive. Based on my observations of your drinking habits so far, I wouldn't place many bets on that happening," Janek said with a mild grin.

"I'll second that. You're like a nurse with your drinks. Each glass of beer feels extremely appreciated and well cared for. Too bad that you can't breastfeed it too," noted Saul, a friend of Albert who was socializing at the apartment.

Thomas had to laugh in response to that comment. *I have to give credit to high-quality wit when it is due. A man breastfeeding a glass of beer; now that is an interesting concept for a theater of the absurd.*

"Who would have ever thought that a glass of beer would be personified with boobs? How did you think of this image, Saul?" Thomas asked.

Saul paused, rubbed his goatee, and then said, "It just came to me in a Eureka moment. Newton has apples fall on his head and I have these kinds of ideas strike me like lightning. Which idea would you say makes a deeper contribution to civilization?"

"Well, for the mass of humankind, they are probably more affected by alcohol. Though Newton's ideas have undoubtedly led to the development of many technologies that have also had an impact on the masses."

"Fair enough. Thank you for momentarily putting me on the same plane as Newton; you are the first person to pull that off with any degree of plausibility."

"I'm honored, Saul. You've probably noticed that my mind is just as twisted as yours."

"If you'll allow me to generalize a little, members of my tribe, or Judaism as it is more commonly called, are often known for verbal creativity. Can I anoint you as an honorary member of my tribe?"

"I'll stew over it tonight while I'm nursing my drink in my bosom," Thomas replied.

"Touché," Saul said.

"By the way, when I was in Paris, I hit it off one night with an Israeli girl at a bar. This reminds me...I should contact her to see how she's doing."

"Ah, Israelis...they are a different breed of Jews. Yes, if you had good chemistry with an Israeli girl, by all means, pursue it."

That is something to chew on. I have not met enough Jews in my lifetime to be able to make any generalizations or observations.

Jews were few and far between in my region of Indiana. Saul was from the north-east somewhere in the U.S., where Jews were much more heavily concentrated. *It would have been nice to have a companion like that back in college,* he reminisced. *I would have felt less lonely if I had had a buddy to throw witty zingers at and then wait in gripping suspense for his equally witty response. It would be analogous to a verbal kind of ping pong.*

Returning to the thought of karaoke, Thomas was a bit intrigued.

"Janek, why do you think that the style of karaoke is different over here?"

Janek paused for a few moments, absorbed in his own mind. "I would say that most likely, the Japanese are too shy on the whole to sing in front of strangers at a bar, even if they have had several drinks. They find it much more comfortable to sing or possibly make a fool out of themselves with their friends or co-workers. It is less intimidating for people who lack extensive singing experience. I've been to a few karaoke bars in the U.S., and when it's crowded, you are required to wait a long time before it's your turn to sing. In the private room with a smaller group, in most cases, the wait is much less."

"Good points. Well, I've never done karaoke in any form. I don't imagine that I'll be doing a lot of singing, but I would like to observe this Japanese custom. It does sound intriguing. What else am I going to do next Saturday anyway? Stare at my cans of tuna in the cupboard?" he said.

When they went out for the karaoke occasion, Thomas was joined by his two roommates and eight other teachers. He had never been on a social outing with this many people before. *Far away on these Japanese shores, I am beginning to resemble a quasi-social organism. We travelers share an intimate bond of mutual curiosity about intangible frontiers. As much as I tried to alienate myself from humanity back home, the same forces simply don't apply here. This is a completely different set of physical laws, with their own forces. These forces cannot produce exactly the same reactions. If it was Newton back in Indiana, it is Einsteinian physics over here. It is nearly impossible for a vastly different set of laws to produce the same counter-force within me. Why try to alienate myself from these teachers? Is there any principle behind this kind of alienation? They are endeavoring to expand their mental horizons and explore this Pacific land, just like myself. They are not content to merely stay at home in the ultra-comfort zone, chugging beers and being determined to stay ignorant about anything beyond American borders. Yes, I might not be an overly extroverted person by nature, but surely it is laudable to make a minimum effort to reach out to them and join them on this musical outing. I might possibly find this experience to be pleasurable. Although there are different physical laws in this social system, these laws are not completely deterministic. The human experience is never completely predetermined; it is full of surprises and jagged turns.*

The enclosed karaoke room was very compatible with the neatly pressed ties and immaculate suits of the Japanese salarymen. Crumbs and clutter were few and far between. Thomas was impressed by the sleek design. There were Japanese prints of Kyoto photos on the wall to accompany the comfortable red couches. There were wooden shelves next to the large TV screen where they would see the song lyrics. Wood seemed to be a common material in Japan. He admired how the Japanese used wood to create appealing artistic appearances; some of the bridges that he had crossed in the city were constructed out of fine wooden material.

In addition to alcohol, the group ordered some Japanese bar-type snacks for the evening. The waitress brought small pieces of tonkatsu, yakitori, smoked eggplant, and octopus balls for the adventurous. Janek insisted that they order this dish to prove that they were true explorers. Thomas was leery of the price of the item: nearly fifteen dollars for these balls alone. *Sure, we're being more "exploratory", Janek; I hope that you like exploring personal statements of debt with these kind of spending habits.* On the other hand, he realized that he only lived (in Japan) once, and it wasn't a completely absurd idea to sample a different kind of dish that was quite rare across the Pacific.

Janek explained that the Japanese liked to have food with their alcohol; this was why the karaoke room (or "karaoke box" as it was often called in Japan) had a fairly extensive food menu. The thinking was also that the food added an additional element to the social experience that mere drinks alone could not provide. Thomas saw the logic of this kind of thinking, and he did not have any vociferous objections to this point. From a health standpoint as well, he could also see that it made sense to mix alcohol consumption with solid foods. Possibly it discouraged excessively fast drinking if there was food present to complicate the experience. However, it clearly did not prevent imbibing in large amounts; the heavily intoxicated young Japanese people coming out of the karaoke box were ample evidence of this trend.

There was a large remote that was used to operate the song selection on the TV screen. If Janek had been absent, they would have had to ask for assistance from the staff. Predictably, he had already been to several karaoke boxes during his previous stopover in Japan. Since he spent most of his evenings socializing, it would have been quite statistically improbable if he had never been to a karaoke box up to this point. *Yes, all schmooze paths eventually led to these musical boxes.* Singing and drinking with others was an integral part of the culture here, in a divergent way from the Western countries.

Albert said he would not be the first to sing. "There is no way in hell that I am singing until I am completely sloshed on the floor...hearing me before that will not be a pretty sight!"

Saul replied, "I'm not going to be the guinea pig either tonight. Possibly I could be the pig in the group since I don't eat them most days, being a virtuous Jew. But the guinea pig? That is completely out of the question!"

"Alright, you cowards, I'll do the first song. But all of you are going to do some kind of singing tonight. At a minimum, you can participate in a group song," Janek said.

"Yes, sir," Thomas replied, and he promptly did a military salute to his forehead.

Janek lightly chuckled. "Thomas, trust me, you're going to enjoy this experience. It's a bit like jumping into the pool for the first time. It would be misguided to think that there would be no anxiety whatsoever when you come to a karaoke box for the first time."

Janek opened the evening by choosing "Sweet Caroline". It sounded a bit odd hearing this tune on the urban, foreign streets of Kyoto. There were very few Carolines here. *Of course you had to pick a mainstream, popular song, Janek. I will definitely choose a more imaginative song. A person's song selection at karaoke reflects something about his character, just as the kind of music that people like reflects character.* Thomas had never been drawn to country music because it was very slow and optimistic; that did not match his inner psyche in the least. He strongly preferred a lot of English rock since it was more stoic, gritty, and tending in a more melancholic direction. The undertones of English rock related well to his often-depressed thoughts. The human experience had a quite different feel in English rock compared to country music; many songs portrayed life as full of a lot of anxiety and angst. Often when Thomas listened to these songs, he was relieved that he was not the only person who frequently experienced this kind of angst and subdued emotion. The mood of "Sweet Caroline" reminded him of his happy-go-lucky, heavy-drinking classmates back in college. That was another reason why he was mildly irritated with Janek (as usual) about this song selection.

A few of the other teachers then sang after Janek in various genres. Katherine, a British lady, chose a song from the musical "Chicago". Thomas did enjoy this song more, though she was a quite average singer. Another teacher, named Floyd, sang Bon Jovi's "You Give Love a Bad Name". He had become brave enough to attempt a song after a couple of beers, though he often just spoke the lyrics rather than singing them. Even after a couple of drinks, Floyd still seemed to fear how people would react upon hearing his singing voice. The alcohol had loosened his inhibitions somewhat, but not completely. Possibly he would need three or four more beers before he completely stopped fretting about others' opinions of his voice.

Thomas decided to take his turn after Floyd. *I do not want to leave this "box" wondering how it would have turned out if I had sung something. With that as a precondition, it makes sense to sing earlier rather than later; otherwise, I will just have anticipation anxiety for most of the evening.*

He selected "Strawberry Fields Forever" by the Beatles. This was a short song, so if it went poorly, he wouldn't be forced to continue his misery for several minutes. John Lennon sang at a lower pitch, so he wouldn't need to belt out a bunch of high notes and possibly destroy his vocal cords. Finally, the song appealed to him. It had a nostalgic feeling, and it was lightly emotional without feeling obnoxious. He liked a lot of the lyrics. "Nothing is real" was an interesting metaphysical idea, and he was also fond of the part that said, "No one I think is in my tree, I mean it must be high or low."

The lyrics appeared on the screen, and his lips froze. Thomas was hardly able to get the first line out. But his voice gradually returned to normal, and he stopped shaking. He was able to sing the remainder of the lyrics. His singing had provoked a strong reaction; nobody was just sitting there, unfazed. Although it was true that English rock tended to be more stoic, this was not the vibe that he was sensing. He wasn't sure why the reaction was turning this way. After he finished, another American teacher named Kara said, "Thomas! You have some talent!" All of the teachers clapped enthusiastically. He was even able to wipe the customary smirk off of Janek's face for a minute. He liked Albert's comment the best. Albert said, "That was badass, man! You did that after only one beer!"

He was hoping that he would not fall flat on his face, so to speak, and the opposite had happened. Evidently, he had some singing ability! He had never thought of himself as a singer before. It wasn't that he had been rejected by choirs or other musical groups. He merely had never attempted musical pursuits. *It isn't a predetermined realm that we live in. Hidden thunderbolts are often just around the curve, even though they are completely unbeknownst to us.*

He briefly considered singing another song for the evening, but the group was only staying in the room for a couple of hours, and there were still quite a few teachers who desired to attempt a song. These rooms were paid by the hour, and they were quite expensive. He definitely considered this to be the priciest "box" that he had ever set foot in; his sandbox at home during childhood was quite a bit cheaper, on an hourly basis. It was quite a stretch to imagine his mother charging him ten dollars per hour merely to play in his sandbox. That was almost tantamount to child abuse.

Although he was deprived of any more soliloquies that evening, Thomas was coaxed into a group song towards the end of the night. He contributed his five cents to "American Pie". It was quite a sappy, cheesy song for his generally brooding psyche, but the fact that the song had the word "American" in it brought back flashbacks from his roots. Images of walking into a grocery store without language barriers came to mind. He also thought of watching English-language movies without the distraction of Japanese subtitles.

Don McLean's classic tune was the penultimate song of the evening. A couple female teachers ended the evening with Journey's "Don't Stop Believin'". Inside, he recoiled in disgust when he heard the song. He felt that their music was far too ordinary and pedestrian. Indeed, Thomas was utterly determined to be buried alive before singing a Journey song at karaoke. Later in his life when karaoke had become a regular habit, Thomas would learn that this was an extremely common karaoke song—actually, a cliché. Avoiding clichés was a paramount feature of his identity. He would rather be burned at the stake, Joan of Arc style, than have someone notice him singing anything by Journey in a public setting. Those were the two main lessons of the night: he had learned that he had singing skill, and that he despised Journey.

As he walked back to the apartment with his roommates, Janek gave him a firm pat on the back. "You are a future performer, Thomas. You're getting lots of practice with public speaking here in the classroom; use it to your advantage," he said.

"Next time we go to another karaoke box, you need to enjoy the alcohol and the singing," Albert noted.

"I appreciate the encouragement, Albert, but I am quite pleased with the outing tonight. Never in my wildest speculation would I have predicted that I would sing a Beatles song and that people would be impressed by my performance. That surprise is of far greater value to me than alcohol," he replied snarkily.

Albert's face was amused. "You're missing the bigger picture. The drinking adds to the enjoyment of the evening. It doesn't take away from your singing ability or musical pleasure in any form. It's a supplement to the karaoke box experience, not a substitute for the singing part."

"Well, suit yourself, Albert. I have no regrets about the evening, other than having my ears polluted with Journey at the end."

"Amen to that, brother. I'm totally with you on the Journey hatred train."

A couple of months had now passed. It was no longer a shock for him to be the only white person in a supermarket, or on a train. He had grown quite accustomed to standing out. He still did not feel comfortable with the Japanese formality or indirect style of speaking, but it felt tantamount to a customary aspect of life now rather than the shock to the system that he had experienced on the plane or during his first few weeks in the country. He certainly did not feel that he "belonged", and he highly doubted that he would ever feel strongly at ease in this society. But Thomas could not deny the fact that he had been able to try many different kinds of food and have some unique experiences that he would have lacked in most other corners of the earth.

He had also become accustomed to yanking the English sen-tences out of his students. He viewed it as analogous to a laborer who toils profusely every day on a farm or inside a factory. It was arduous work, but it was not volunteer work. After all he was receiving financial compensation for his verbal dental procedures. He would get the English words out of their mouths, come hell or high water. Occasionally he entertained the thought of enrolling in dental school when he returned to the United States; performing a root canal would be quite effortless compared to teaching some of his classes. *Yes, I could do a root canal. Alimentary, my dear Watson.*

He felt that now would be an opportune time to "check in" with Sendi, his Israeli potential love interest. Would she still remember him from that crowded bar in Paris? He sent her a short email, asking her for a "life update". A couple of days later, she responded:

"Thomas,

Of course I remember you! You are very sincere, genuine man. I do not forget this type man easily. I have now returned to Israel. I search for work now. Economy in Israel is uneven. I am happy to be eating my country's food again. Hummus in France is not the same as home. It is good that you are learning Japanese culture. When you finish your teaching, my invitation to come to Israel is still open. Israeli hospitality is eternal, ha ha. Write again soon, Sendi"

She is so to the point, Thomas thought. There is no struggle communicating with her. Thoughts of an Israeli voyage and mouth-watering hummus were quite intriguing, but finishing "his mission" in Japan was of paramount concern at the moment. He was a cultural soldier here, battling the struggles of foreign speakers of English. It was his quasi-duty to complete the year-long teaching contract. It was happenstance that he had connected with Sendi that evening in Paris; he couldn't allow that evening to determine every decision. He firmly believed that if this relationship was meant to endure, a year-long contract would not be a massive impediment. If it were destiny that they would fall in love, a year was a mere grain of sand on this metaphorical beach.

Shifting his focus to his day-to-day essence, just as he had explored parts of France as a tourist, he was equally determined not to ignore this aspect of his stay in Japan. Casual sightseeing offered a welcome break from the grind of the daily routine, as well as a different angle on the culture and history of this idiosyncratic land. Moreover, he was living in the tourist mecca of Japan. *It would be heinous sacrilege to neglect sites that were literally a stone's throw away from my home and language institute. If I absorb myself too much in my daily life and neglect exploring the astounding city of Kyoto, then I have fallen into the similar insular traps that I castigated my former college classmates for falling into.* It wasn't the *same* trap since he was still having a very exotic experience merely by living in Japan. When he sat on a commuter train and was the only white person on the train, this was in itself something quite distinct from his experiences in Indiana. Every day as he taught students, he constantly felt the cultural gap between them and him. It was a language gap and cultural gap amalgamated into one metaphorical wall of distance.

Although it would not be the same type of trap, it would still be regrettable if he failed to take advantage of the tourist opportunities that were on his doorstep. Of course, nothing prevented him from eventually returning to Japan. But it would never again be this easy to travel in Japan (or Asia generally). Future trips would require long, excruciating plane rides combined with horrendous jet lag from the sizable time difference between Japan and the United States.

On a pleasant, mild day in February, he went out by himself to explore two of the extremely famous temples in Kyoto: Kinkakuji Temple and Kiyomizu-dera Temple. Kyoto had hundreds of temples, and he considered the virtues of exploring off the beaten path into more obscure, less well-known temples. Although this approach fit in well with several aspects of his contrarian nature, he was not persuaded that it was the best course of action. He was unconvinced that there was anything detrimental about beginning with the most famous temples. Thomas believed that there are usually valid reasons why a tourist site becomes quite famous. Sites rarely become randomly well known.

Even if he found that an extremely famous temple did not match the hype of common expectations, nevertheless, it was a valuable experience to compare his impression with those expectations. Second, there is a strong desire of most humans to experience famous places. If he were to travel somewhere and ignore the most famous sites, he would later have a quite nagging "what if" feeling. *What if I had explored the most famous temples? Would I have been enthralled with them?* He was strongly in favor of "off the beaten path" type of travel, but he also saw tremendous value in the conventional famous sites. He did not see these competing principles as mutually exclusive. The richest travel was to combine both.

He had now arrived at Kinkakuji. He purchased a ticket and an audio tour. Audio tours were available in Japanese, English, French, German, Spanish, Chinese, and Korean. *This seems to cover quite a wide swathe of humanity. They must receive large numbers of visitors from their East Asian neighbors, even though there is deeply entrenched bitterness between Japan and these nations from Japan's imperialist past.* He realized that, nonetheless, people have a strong desire to visit places that might have wronged their land in the past. The Irish continued to work and travel in England, and many Latin Americans traveled to Spain each year.

He thought that there was a clear benefit for the conquered to see their conqueror entity with their own eyes as tourists. It could help to build a future understanding between the two nations if Koreans met kind ordinary Japanese people, for example. They could see that the whole of Japanese humanity was not exclusively represented by the violent butchering of days gone by. The Japanese military was a component of the society, but it did not represent every element in its periodic table. There were Carbon Dioxides to counter the Oxygens.

Furthermore, if Korean or Chinese tourists were to experience a beautiful temple or stunning Japanese garden, would this experience at all assuage the pain of the past? It seemed unlikely that this would be a universal reaction; it would most likely vary among individual people. Most likely, some would cling to seething resentment regardless of any pleasurable experiences during the visit. Others, however, probably would espouse this more even-handed view. The conquered would not forgive the conquerors merely from these experiences, or amend their views about the conquerors' culpability. It could assuage the pain, however, by seeing that the conquering land was a mixed, nuanced picture of good and evil, vice and virtue. The headache would not be completely ameliorated, but it could be reduced from a migraine to a weaker pain by seeing this nuanced picture. This was his hope as he observed Chinese and Korean tourists walking through the temple grounds. *It is unlikely that the ones who were completely resentful would have made this trip. To the contrary, these tourists were part of a self-selected class who wanted to grow by sensing the larger, more intricate viewpoint.* Thomas knew from his own life that the decision to leave native borders usually entailed wanting to experience a larger, more nuanced reality. Those who had the black and white view that everything in Japan was evil would have abstained from this trip.

He was firmly convinced that it was not inevitable that tourism became reduced to crass commercialism. Thomas had a few shades of optimism that inter-cultural understanding could emerge from the hordes of people who breathed the air and smelled the scents of nature as they sauntered through Kinkakuji. His viewpoint was firm that this event today was not merely "something to do" for these tourists. Possibly it was for the young children who were accompanying their parents. Within the sub-population of adults, however, he did not believe that it was just a pedestrian happening.

Thomas began earnestly listening to his audio tour in English. He was not a member of the conquered population, and it was now time to turn inward and immerse himself in his surroundings. The tour noted that the grounds of the temple were originally a villa that had been acquired by Shogun Ashikaga Yoshimitsu in the fourteenth century. A complex was built on the grounds and then, after his death, Yoshimitsu's son converted the complex into a Zen temple.

He was now struck by another quintessential "Japan" moment. He was unquestionably right now in Japan. He was walking on grounds that were acquired by a shogun! This was not France, nor China, nor Egypt. Where else in the world had shoguns existed? Indisputably, Japan had a unique history, and he was walking in it. He was strolling through a limited-edition type of place within the spectrum of human experiences. Somewhat childishly, the thought entered his mind that he could run, but not hide from the legacy of the shoguns in Japan, especially in Kyoto. Shogun footprints were ubiquitous. In order to elude these footprints, it would be necessary to depart from Japan.

He also found it noteworthy that this was a Zen Buddhist temple. This was not quintessentially Japanese. Thomas knew that Buddhism had not originated in Japan. One of the other teachers in the program, Jane, claimed that Japan was "far less Buddhist" than Thailand, where she had also taught English. He knew that Zen Buddhism emphasized seated meditation. Japan did not seem to be a nation of monks by any means; the stressed-out businessmen that he had seen in the modern part of the city hardly seemed Buddhist, as he understood the term.

However, he could see some connection between seated medi-tation and the quiet nature of the Japanese. Had Zen Buddhism influenced this characteristic, or was it due to other factors? It could be just as plausible to argue that the Japanese were quieter than a lot of other cultures because they were afraid of offending others. It is more difficult for a person to speak if he is anxious about antagonizing others. If he had traveled to other Asian nations that are also influenced by Buddhism, it would give him a much more thorough picture. Were they as reserved in the other Asian nations?

I would like to discuss this topic with Jane. If they were much less reserved in other nations that were part of the "Buddhist cluster", then this would strongly refute any link between quietude and Buddhism. But as speculation, it seems to have some merit as a beginning point of investigation. Jane will love this conversation. She can show off her Asian travels and act as an authority on Buddhism's influence. He could not fault Jane for wanting to flaunt her knowledge of other places. He was beginning to gain some pride from his foreign experiences; it was reasonable to think that others would react in the same way.

For a minute, he imagined having several Asian stamps on

his passport rather than merely one. The joys of international travel could also turn into a hornet's nest; he wasn't content with merely capturing the rook in this metaphorical chess game. He also coveted the bishop, knight, and queen. But realistically, he was still quite a young man, and his fate had not been sealed; there would be more prospects for Asian adventure down the road. He had chosen Japan as an easier first step into Asia, but surely it would be tragic if his Asian experience completely ended on this relatively small island. The huge land mass of China was practically a hop, skip, and jump away. He was quite intrigued about Thailand as well from his sundry conversations with Jane. Travel was a bottomless pit for the sufficiently curious. The mere fact that an entity was bottomless did not imply that he should lounge at the top. Likewise, he was aware that some physicists were searching for a "theory of everything". This seemed to be a similar type of endeavor; the likelihood of developing a theory of everything was analogous to being able to travel everywhere that a person desired in his lifetime.

The next section of the audio tour described the architecture of Kinkakuji. The lady narrating the tape mentioned that each of the three floors of the temple had a distinct style of architecture. The first floor was built in the Shinden style, which modeled the living style of the Heian imperial aristocracy from the eleventh century. The floor had open spaces and natural-looking wood which emphasized the natural scenery around the building. This was consistent with a lot of the physical backdrop of Kyoto; Japanese gardens were very common, and there seemed to be a strong appreciation for nature. He considered it impressive on some levels that such a dense, crowded country nevertheless made a considerable attempt to preserve the beauty of nature. Certainly the general tendency of crowded places was to destroy nature in favor of immediate human needs (this was akin to a kind of anti-gentrification). New York City was famous for Central Park, but he had never heard that New York City was particularly famous for nature. He googled on his phone the population of Japan around 1400; it was estimated to be between eight and twelve million people. Clearly, it was far less densely populated at that time compared to now. But regardless, the Japanese had preserved many of these natural relics and there were still a myriad number of Japanese gardens in his surroundings. Despite the significant population growth that had occurred since that period, they had not abandoned their emphasis on nature; they had still managed to value it, despite the jam-packed conditions of the country. He found this to be admirable. Clearly values that had developed over several centuries had not been completely abandoned.

Would these traditional values survive another couple hundred years of globalization? Two hundred years from now, would these gardens still be there, or would Japan merely look like everywhere else, filled with sprawl and fast food chains? The latter possibility certainly sounded like fruitful material for a dystopian novel. He was aware from his experiences talking to students that Japan was changing at a rapid pace. However, he remained cautiously optimistic that Japan would never completely lose its unique essence, and that it would still be an inimitable land for the great-great-grandchildren of his generation. It was likely that dystopian novels were entertaining to write, but to imagine that these dystopias were actually real was extremely disheartening.

The second floor was built in a samurai style, according to the audio. Sliding wooden doors evoked a theme of transience. There was also a Buddha hall and a Buddhist shrine that was devoted to Kannon, the goddess of mercy. It seemed logical that a samurai theme would call attention to transience. Death (both voluntary and involuntary) was most likely at the forefront of the samurai warrior's mind; death was in clear opposition to permanence. *Yes, a culture that promoted the "honor" of suicide certainly espoused a transient lifestyle. Was there any act that was more transient than suicide? Homicide was a very distant second with regard to transience since it was a less controlled death. Suicide, intentional death, was the epitome of transience. Here today, gone tomorrow is a very grotesque simplification of this disconcerting action.*

Next, the obvious question was why was there a goddess of mercy on a floor that had a samurai theme? *Weren't the samurai famous for not showing mercy?* This level of "opinionated analysis" was not covered in his audio tour. No, when the lady on the tape came to the topic of the shrine, she spent five minutes describing in elaborate detail the materials of the shrine and the process that went into building it. That did not hold his interest compared to the question that he had just formulated. He did the equivalent of blowing off the tour guide (he turned off the tape), and instead, he researched this question on his phone again. How did people cope thirty years ago when they could not immediately research questions? He might have committed honor suicide, samurai style, from the frustration of not having a smartphone. (Images of a samurai warrior exclaiming "I lost my phone" and then plunging his sword into his stomach entered his mind.) And then he never would have learned about the relationship between the samurai and mercy.

According to Dr. Google, the samurai followed teachings that were called the Bushido code. This code had eight general principles. Some of them were unsurprising, such as honor, courage, and loyalty. But one of the principles was mercy. The samurai were taught to show mercy for different social classes, and to strike a balance in war. It seemed to be the case that the samurai were much more like medieval knights than brutes; Thomas realized that his original images of the samurai were very simplified caricatures. They were not merely "macho, tough" men. No, they had an elaborate code of ethics that was also heavily influenced by Shintoism; their strong respect for their ancestors was one effect of these teachings. They were expected to show a balance in war and use virtuous judgment. Although the Japanese had committed unspeakable atrocities during their colonial rule of their neighbors, this was not how the samurai were taught to behave. Instead, a true samurai would view the actions of these modern Japanese conquerors as a horrific departure from his code of ethics.

Ever since he had begun his journey to Japan, it was readily apparent that this was a very convoluted land. The term "convoluted" did not begin to describe the puzzles and paradoxes of this culture. If "convoluted" were a person, he would say to this person: "You think that you're complicated? You're a raging simpleton compared to these folks!" The Bushido code seemed to be a straightforward extension of the enigmatic nature of the Japanese. Samurai behavior was complicated. They were not simply government-sanctioned gangsters.

He glowed inside. He had discovered this more complex reality about the samurai. Now, he considered this day at Kinkakuji to be especially valuable. It was quite unlikely that he would have learned these facts about the samurai from picking up a book. He hadn't been able to read extensively during his time in Japan. During the week, he was exhausted from the long teaching hours, and on the weekend, he often wanted to explore. Sure, he had been able to do some sporadic reading on the train when commuting to work and he often read for short portions of the weekend. But he would not be setting any records for "book consumption" in the immediate future. No book publishers were about to become filthy rich from his reading productivity. Fortunately, despite his reading limitations in his current circumstances, he had learned about the fascinating complexity of the samurai.

Instead, the visual experience of witnessing a goddess of mercy on a samurai-dominated floor had forced him to examine his preconceived notions. Again, he realized why it was problematic to always be "comfortable". If he were always confined to comfortable, familiar, situations, then these assumptions would never be challenged. The prickly nature of the travel beast was intimately linked with the character-building spirit of foreign travel. Darkness had to be balanced with light. Out of the darkness came photons of light that moved towards personal enlightenment. After this learning experience, he felt one centimeter closer to personal enlightenment. He was no Buddha or infallible being, but he was making slow, gradual movements in a virtuous direction. Daily life here was a road with many potholes, as was the case in Indiana. But it was refreshing to know that buried among the rubble of this angst and frequent melancholy emotions were these sparks of light. It was critical to have these sparks of light. Their existence made him feel that his life was not completely hollow. He had not toiled as a talking monkey in vain.

The moment had now arrived to ascend to the third, final floor. This extrasensory experience was nearing its final lap. Thomas would be obliged to return to the modern Japanese world in a little while. The third level had a Zen Buddhist style. The mood up here was much more religious compared to the other floors.

From a spatial point of view, he could see why the temple would be built this way. The first floor was closest to the physical ground and had a nature theme. The middle floor emphasized the samurai human history; humans came after plants and animals in the history of time. Finally, the third floor was closest to the "heavens", where people attempt to escape from the status quo and shift their attention to a different realm.

He did not know if this temple was built with these exact themes in mind, but if it were the case, he could understand the logical reasoning behind the design. Even if the design had different original intentions, did it matter? This was how Thomas chose to internalize his experience of the temple; the actual facts seemed irrelevant in comparison. This was an essential component of the travel process: as a traveler, he was bombarded with constant sensory stimuli, and in order for this experience to have a deeper meaning, the sensations had to be assimilated into some kind of schema. The next traveler behind him at the airport or down the hall at his language school would have, at a minimum, a somewhat different schema. The same sensory impressions would then be molded into a different schema. It was not possible for any two individuals to have the same schema. On the contrary, the vast possibilities of the human mind caused a nearly infinite number of schemas to exist. International travel would be far less seductive if this were not the case.

Thomas was now thoroughly satisfied with his stroll through Kinkakuji, and he felt that he had reached the saturation point. There was a finite limit to how much he could absorb from any one site. Although he had reached the saturation point here at Kinkakuji, he had not reached the saturation point today for visiting temples. Kinkakuji had piqued his curiosity, and he decided to continue with the original plan to also visit

Kiyomizu-dera. One of his favorite comedians, Lewis Black, often talked about the "mood" during his comedy routines and he would emphasize the word by making it sound as if it had come from a cow: mooood. Channeling Lewis Black, Thomas was unquestionably in a "temple mooood" today. Five years ago, he never would have imagined that he would wake up one day in a temple mooood, but this added to the pile of life's revelations. He had an uncle who woke up craving alcohol, and he knew numerous people who woke up with sugar cravings. But today, he, Thomas Gephardt, contrarian-in-chief, had woken up in a temple mood. Therefore, he would go into severe withdrawal if he did not explore another temple. Inevitably, Amy Winehouse's song "Rehab" entered his mind: "They tried to make me go to [temple] rehab, but I said, 'No, No, No!'"

As he found his way to Kiyomizu-dera, he observed once again that there was an option to purchase an audio tour. However, after one temple, his "battery" had lost a lot of power. He felt as if he had returned to the beach in Majorca, and was attempting to get out of the water, but the waves kept pushing him back. No, this tour would be a bit more on the abridged side. Although he had not reached the temple saturation point at this juncture, he could not stomach another full audio tour.

It was no shocker to learn that Kiyomizu-dera was another ancient Buddhist temple and a UNESCO World Heritage Site. It had been originally founded in 778, which was a good seven hundred years before Columbus had landed on American shores. The current buildings were constructed in 1633, which made it quite the spring chicken compared to Kinkakuji. However, it was difficult to sense a tangible difference of "ancientness" or "historicity" between the two temples. At some basic level, "old" was old. *At what point does a site become "old" in the eyes of the observer?* Age was fundamentally subjective. He recalled a quite memorable witticism from Mark Twain: "Age is an issue of mind over matter. If you don't mind, it doesn't matter."

As he continued roaming around the ancient grounds of Kiyomizu-dera, he noticed a large group of young Japanese tourists. They were wearing school uniforms, so they certainly were not older than eighteen. The girls were wearing the traditional skirts that characterized Japanese school attire. Their focus didn't seem to be on the temple itself; rather they were taking group pictures. Not just a few pictures. No, this was not a short story equivalent of picture taking. This was more analogous to "War and Peace"-style picture taking. This story must have had a beginning at some point, it was reasonable to assume. However, it was not self-evident that there would be an end. When the writers of the Declaration of Independence talked about holding truths to be self-evident, they did not have the end of this story in mind. It was a group of ten girls and three boys. Each person was intent on taking lots of pictures of the group with his or her fancy camera, and the others often took quite goofy poses, accompanied by generous portions of giggling. *If it were possible to become fat from consuming giggles, it would definitely happen to this group.*

He hoped that this group was not going to load all of their photos to Flickr. Thomas worried that the website would run out of capacity if this were to happen. *Flickr may need to expand their data storage to the craters of the moon if this group starts uploading pictures! They clearly are not in awe of this temple compared to me. Probably since they have grown up in Kyoto, this temple is merely part of the landscape. Buddhism to them is like a hamburger to Americans; it is rather pedestrian. If I had grown up here, I doubt that I would feel impressed by this temple either.*

Why are they taking so many pictures of each other? Is this a competition? Or are they merely releasing tension from their busy school lives? He realized that he had never seen a self-contained group that was this self-absorbed. It seemed quite plausible that he could throw a rock through a window and they would be completely oblivious to it. *Perhaps if the smashing glass is close enough, it will enter their pictures on the periphery; that seems to be the only means by which they would notice.*

He was cognizant of the fact that young people in all societies often exhibited wacky behavior; Japanese youngsters did not own a patent on this conduct. Yet, he could never remember being quite this puzzled from observing children in the United States. He had many recollections of feeling annoyed by American children, but being annoyed was quite different than feeling baffled.

At the end of the day (or marathon picture-taking session), Thomas realized again that he would never understand this culture. He did not feel any angst from this realization; it was merely a fact that he would have to accept in order to avoid going bonkers in Japan. *No, I will not deprive myself of sleep tonight, attempting to understand these adolescents. Japan is not a maze that has a shiny box wrapped in glitzy red ribbon at the end. Rather, a Japanese maze has an end that is more disorienting than the beginning. Grasping Japanese culture moves in a "Benjamin Button" direction with time. By the end of the journey, I will feel that I was quite enlightened when I first started.* He had spent enough time in Japan now to be thoroughly reconciled to this reality.

Before today, he had already abandoned any hope of attaining a sense of understanding about the culture here. Therefore, this observation of the Japanese youths did not alter any trajectory; it merely added another stone to an existing pile. If anything, it was comforting on one level that he had fully accepted this reality. Perhaps in some contexts, ignorance really was bliss. Striving towards a realizable goal was laudable; attempting to obtain the impossible, on the other hand, was tomfoolery. If, as Einstein said, insanity was doing the same thing over and over and expecting different results, then turbo insanity was endeavoring to think that he would ever be something other than a clueless gaijin here.

When he had first arrived at the airport, he noticed how much he stood out externally as a white man. He was now quite accustomed to this facet of his quotidian life. Now his perception of estrangement was nothing external; it was an utterly psychological phenomenon. In a Japanese crowd, he was the shoe that didn't fit; he was at peace with this reality. He had never wanted to be the shoe that fit all the time anyway; that was a colorless existence. Although white was not considered a "color" on the human race spectrum, his intention of leading a colorful life was metaphorical rather than an external fact of his appearance. Adding color to his life did not involve attempting to appear more like the Japanese in a Michael Jackson-like fashion. This too was a psychological condition, not a physical one.

After he had fully recovered from the shock of observing the manic young photographers near him, he immersed his twisted mind in a few more relics on the Kiyomizu-dera grounds, and then left. He could not spend any more time at temples today. The marginal utility of any additional temple time would be zero. No, actually it would have a negative value, because he would be irked that he was loitering in a place where he had reached his mental saturation point instead of switching gears and participating in a more worthwhile activity. A marginal utility of zero seemed to reflect a calm, detached state of mind. Such a description of his mental state if he went to another temple would be a fabrication of reality. Thomas had strong doubts that his mental states ever truly had a marginal utility of zero; his psyche had too much turmoil.

Although he was now a null member of the set of people who would be able to enjoy a temple for the remainder of this day, it was still light out, and the sun would not set for a few more hours. If tourism was his job today, then it was inefficient to revert back to his bidet-containing abode right now. He had become quite fond of the toilets in Japan; they had elaborate features that were rarely found outside of Japanese borders. Water squirted up into the anus as a means of cleaning, and in public places, after one person finished sitting on the toilet, a new set of plastic was automatically rotated onto the seat for the next lucky turd artist. He was familiar with the Spanish expression "mi casa es tu casa", which was a form of hospitality, essentially saying that my house is your house; make yourself at home. If he ever needed to host a visitor at his dwelling here, he would welcome the visitor by saying, "my anus-washing toilet is your anus-washing toilet." Indeed, the toilet was the most important feature of someone's home; therefore, it was quite important to incorporate this uplifting fixture into the visitor's welcome.

He was within the general vicinity of the geisha district. This was just what the talking monkey ordered; it would be a satisfying change of pace from the temple exploration. It was now time for more instantaneous Google research on his smartphone. He knew little about geisha women. His research found that the Kyoto geisha district was called Gion. Apparently, the geisha in this district and throughout most of Kyoto called themselves geiko. He found this to be a rather unfortunate coincidence with English; could he save 300 yen on his renter's insurance by switching from geisha to geiko? He wondered if any of the geiko here had heard of Geico. Had any employees of Geico ever visited this district? Since it was quite famous, the probability that this had transpired was quite high.

He also found it a bit ironic that these terms had such a similar sound; could there be any greater contrast in their essence? Geico was known for providing cheap, basic car insurance. The geiko, on the other hand, were known for elaborate dress and rituals. If a geiko had Geico insurance, it would be quite the skeleton in her cupboard. Based on his quite inadequate knowledge of being a geisha, he could think of no greater cause of shame for a geiko. Even being confused with a gecko seemed to be much more honorable than switching to Geico. His head was beginning to hurt from the geiko-Geico-gecko triumvirate. Damn phonetics in different languages!

As he continued reading about the geisha, the article stated that Gion was divided into five communities, or hanamachi. Gion Kobu was by far the largest hanamachi, and it occupied most of the district. He could see from the geographic description that he was indeed currently walking in Gion Kobu; he had not by chance stumbled into one of the smaller areas.

The streets of Gion were filled with machiya (old townhouses), and some of these were ochaya (tea houses). This was where the geisha practiced their craft. They were not prostitutes; instead, the geisha entertained wealthier men through singing, dancing, games, conversation, etc. He had briefly talked to Martin, another English teacher in his program. Martin had also taught in South Korea, and had talked about the existence of "room salons"; these room salons sounded quite similar to the ochaya in that the women entertained the male clients and provided companionship, but not sex. However, for some reason, the term geisha (or even geiko if one could forget about the car insurance company) sounded much more charming than anything associated with a "room salon". The term room salon seemed to connote something dirty, even if it was not intended to do so. Thomas was quite fond of the term "geisha"; it had a nice sound to it and rolled off the tongue quite smoothly.

Nobody would confuse the geisha with contemporary Japanese people. They wore old, traditional clothing. He saw a few come in and out of the ochaya; they were wearing kimonos, tabi (buttoned socks), large wigs, and okobo (large wooden sandals). Most of them carried hand fans with them as well. Some were walking with umbrellas that looked akin to large hand fans. Clearly, the hand fan was an essential part of the geisha essence. He could imagine that these were a useful performance tool, and could provide some comfort as well during Japan's summers, which were dreadfully humid. It was quite entertaining merely to observe them in the street; what would it be like to actually be entertained by one? He knew that the price of geisha entertainment greatly exceeded his teacher salary, but it was intriguing to imagine what the experience would be.

Since he had been on foreign soil, Thomas had been almost boasting in his mind about how much access he was having to phenomenal experiences. Over and over, he kept repeating the mantra that it was better to witness a place firsthand rather than merely imagine it; sensory perception was superior to armchair rationalizing, he kept saying to himself. But now, temporarily, he had been stopped in his tracks. He would be denied sensory access to a true "geisha" experience. He would only be able to muse from his philosophically tormented armchair with ripped existential fabric. Thomas comforted himself with the fact that he was still leaps and bounds ahead of most of the rest of humanity with regard to the sensory observations; he had *seen* geisha walking in the street. How many Americans (or non-Japanese people generally) could say that?

He still felt as though he were at the track meet; he just would not have prime access to the high-jump bar or the long-jump pit. For this experience, he would have to settle for pretty good rather than outstanding. There was no reason to feel disheartened. "Do not let the perfect be the enemy of the good" was a cliché, but it seemed to be the right expression in this circumstance. It wasn't that grand of a leap to transition from seeing geisha in the street to imagining how the full experience was. No traveler could witness everything that he wanted to see anyway; that was a return to his "traveler's theory of everything", which was impossible to attain. No, this glass was ninety percent full today. He had walked through two magnificent temples, and now he was breathing the air of the geisha district of Kyoto, which was yet another unique wrinkle in this highly unusual, somewhat bizarre civilization.

Physically, he was now completely at his saturation point. There would be no more exploring today. A comfortable bed and some home-cooked food began to feel quite appealing. However, there was one question that was still nagging at his psyche from today's experiences. *What did the geisha institution suggest, if anything, about the status of women in Japan? Was it sexist?* They were not sex workers or strippers, so it did not seem to objectify women in that manner. They did learn skills that went far beyond mere sexual appeal such as singing, dancing, etc. Certainly a geisha's wardrobe was infinitely less demeaning than a stripper's one. His understanding was that the geisha were being paid to provide non-sexual entertainment. This did not strike Thomas as grossly chauvinist in and of itself. Japan was a deeply chauvinist society; there was no question about that. The mere fact that it was considered "unladylike" for a girl to laugh in public and not cover her mouth certainly seemed to demonstrate this. Furthermore, on the whole, he did not feel that his female Japanese students had as much self-esteem as their Western counterparts, or compared to his female co-teachers in the program. From their vibe, on the whole, he felt quite a bit of meekness and subservience. It was difficult to separate this impression from an "objective" analysis of the geisha institution. He firmly believed that theory preceded observation; our preconceptions highly influence how we think and what we see. This facet of the human mind made it difficult to completely write off the possibility that the geisha institution was sexist.

However, was it possible that the geisha merely *behaved* in a servile fashion because of Japanese culture and not because of the institution itself? He could not see what was inherently sexist about a paid female entertainer who provided non-sexual services. A waitress or an actress also provided a kind of "non-sexual service", in a broader sense as well. Nobody argued that acting was fundamentally sexist; therefore, how was this different in kind? His conclusion from his limited observations today was that if Japanese men treated their geisha with disrespect or in an objectifying way, then it was from cultural influences of the greater society, not because of the specific institution of the geisha. However, he believed that it would be highly fascinating to hear a well-argued viewpoint that opposed his view. Possibly a sound, rational argument could convince him that aspects of the geisha institution were indeed sexist.

Before he left the geisha area, he browsed through a couple of souvenir stands. It was stimulating to observe what kinds of souvenirs were on display here; obviously the souvenirs in Japan were different than those in France. There were small fans, Japanese-style miniature dolls, small kimono-style stick figures, and keychains with various Japanese relics (including a red Japanese-style lamp). He was not particularly in the mood to spend a lot of time browsing through souvenirs due to his intense state of exhaustion. Active tourism certainly required a plentiful amount of energy and stamina. He decided that he would return another day when he was well rested and hadn't spent the last few hours meandering through temples. As he walked away, he briefly looked back, just to validate his decision that he would indeed return another day. When he looked back, he saw that the vendor was double checking everything in her stand, examining if anything was missing.

I've just been profiled. She thinks that I might have stolen some-thing. He had conversed with another teacher in his program, Silvio, who had extensive experience traveling through Asia. This experience brought to mind a comment that Silvio had previously made about Japan. Silvio said, "This is the only place in Asia where whitey isn't king." Silvio had taught in three other Asian countries and he had traveled in eleven or twelve countries. According to him, everywhere else, they looked up to the white man; you were treated better if you were white and because you were white. Japan, for better or worse, had the confidence to stand toe-to-toe with "whitey", or in this case, Thomas felt that he was being scorned, rather than merely occupying an equal plane with the Japanese.

He had felt subtle sentiments in this general area before; he had never felt particularly welcome as a gaijin in Japan, and there were subtle indicators that they would prefer that he take his talking-monkey circus performance somewhere else.

However, up to this point, nothing had been this blatant as openly suspected theft. It was a quite humiliating feeling to be profiled in this manner. *My society has committed wrongs against the Japanese, especially during World War II. I am completely cognizant of this fact, but two wrongs never make a right.*

Was it possible that the owner of this souvenir stand was merely just obsessive compulsive, and she kept a constant count of her inventory throughout the day? This may have been a latent factor in her examination of the stand after he left, but she did not seem to be auditing her inventory after the Japanese customers were leaving. No, he wasn't being paranoid; without a doubt, he had been profiled. Although two wrongs never made a right, it was also true that every cloud had a silver lining. Perhaps he would be more sympathetic now to other groups who endured profiling experiences in the U.S., such as Muslims at airports. Black Americans were also subject to many different kinds of profiling. It was indeed difficult, as an American white man, to understand the nature of this experience. Now his ability to empathize in this context had significantly grown. It was difficult or borderline impossible to refrain from making any generalizations about groups; he made them constantly. But this psychological reality did not alter the fact that it was quite painful to be profiled.

Nearly two opposite statements or tendencies seemed to have equal truth value. What did this suggest about the nature of truth? Were the postmodernists right that truth was an illusion and completely subjective? He thought about this for a few minutes, and he decided that he still vehemently disagreed with the postmodernists. Truth was *not* an illusion. Instead, he recalled the paradox of thrift from his college Economics course. This paradox stated that it might be beneficial for an individual to save large amounts of money, but it was not beneficial for society as a whole since it reduced consumption; what was good for the part was not always good for the whole. This seemed to be an analogous situation. Profiling was clearly harmful to the individual, but often, profiling was based on statistical tendencies that did exist. It was impossible to avoid all generalizations about human groups and completely unrealistic, nor did it seem to have any truth value to completely "abstain" from this activity. It was even conceivable that this particular souvenir vendor *had indeed* witnessed gaijin stealing souvenirs, or she had experienced theft from gaijin at her stand.

However, similar to the paradox of thrift, even if this were true, it did not mitigate Thomas's pain at being profiled. No statistics, rational argument, or "wisdom from experience" could mitigate this pain. Some emotions and experiences were indeed immune to rational arguments, and he did not believe that these experiences lacked truth value, even if they primarily came from emotions rather than logic or scientific rigor.

As Thomas continued the laborious work of teaching English, he did notice one very appealing feature of this job that affected his emotions positively: he was meeting many women in his classes, and many of them were close to his age. In college and life generally, meeting women usually involved more effort. It was usually necessary to "approach" women in various settings, which he had always found to be a struggle. He had difficulty beginning conversations with strangers, and found it wearisome to overcome his initial nerves.

Once he began conversations, continuing them was much easier, assuming that the person wasn't one of those "catatonic" types. He often found many of his students to fit this description, though being catatonic in a foreign, deeply unfamiliar language was quite different than being catatonic in the native tongue. The former reflected language proficiency and confidence, while the latter reflected personality aspects. He believed that you could "run but not hide" from being catatonic in your native language.

Physically, he did not find Japanese women to be in the same league as women in France. He was quite awed by the beauty and style of French women. This was not the case in Japan, but this did not rule out all Japanese women as potential dating material. He was drawn to some from their sweet personalities and striking fashion styles. He rarely saw a Japanese woman whom he would describe as "beautiful", but many of them were definitely "cute".

After he had been teaching for five months, he met one woman taking his classes who particularly interested him: Tomomi Kurosawa. She was a senior at Kyoto University of Art and Design. Since he had also recently graduated from college, their ages were quite close. Tomomi was unquestionably an "artistic" type; she was quite talented at ceramics, painting, and drawing. He was quite enthralled by the sophistication of some of her drawings. She was able to draw three dimensions with impressive depth and creativity, and the drawings evoked much food for thought.

He had not forgotten about Sendi, the Israeli woman whom he had met in Paris, but he wasn't bound by any commitment to her. She was undoubtedly a potential love interest, but he had already vowed not to let her extreme beauty predetermine his international adventures. After teaching Tomomi for a month, he had asked her to have coffee one afternoon. She was quite friendly in class, and not as reserved as many of the other students. He was initially taken aback that she accepted his invitation. She even smiled and her eyes lit up with a bright smile when he asked her. He had sensed some chemistry between them in class (though not biology or physics), and her reaction confirmed his previous initial impressions.

Fortunately, Tomomi did not wear the stratospheric amounts of makeup that he had witnessed on the airplane. Her makeup was a nice balance. It enhanced her appearance, but she was not treading water in a swimming pool of cosmetics. *She had found the Aristotelian middle with regard to cosmetics!*

Their initial conversations were not radically unrelated to their interactions in class; they discussed their interests, hobbies, what movie stars they adored, etc. Tomomi's favorite Hollywood actors were Tom Hanks and Ryan Gosling. She was in good company with hordes of women from other places in being drawn to Ryan Gosling. The fact that she liked Hanks did not surprise Thomas either; Hanks had been in many notable movies that showcased interesting aspects of American culture, such as *Forrest Gump*. Her countenance buzzed with extreme excitement (possibly bordering on ecstasy) whenever they discussed Tom Hanks. Thomas also liked many of Hanks's movies; therefore, this common interest provided good fodder for conversation.

Tomomi spent a large portion of her free time pursuing her artistic interests. One of her paintings had a traditional Japanese garden in exquisite detail. She also showed him a drawing that contained scenes from a typical Kyoto street. The street had five vending machines, a place to find a newspaper, a couple of small restaurant stands, and off in the distance, a Buddhist temple was visible.

As they were examining her work over tea at his apartment, he asked her, "Why do you like art?"

"Eto...I can express feeling. I am Japanese woman. Hard to express feeling other way."

"Interesting. Japan does seem very strict to me. So art allows an outlet for your inner thoughts?"

"Yes."

"Do I allow an outlet for your inner thoughts?" he said with a big grin.

"Sometimes," she replied sheepishly. "It is different part of me. You are nice man. You respect me more than Japanese man that I know."

"Very glad to hear that. You understand me better than the girls back home. I had to cross a couple of oceans to find a girl who could understand me," he chuckled.

She made a big smile when he said that. "It is good that you open to another culture," she said in a very sweet, charming tone of voice.

"That's my life-calling," he replied.

They then chatted for a few more minutes before going to sleep.

The relationship was going so well that Thomas was beginning to become a bit skeptical how long this momentum would last. One of his friends at the language school had made the observation that "good things usually don't last", and being quite a cynic himself, he was inclined to agree with this sentiment. He had an especially delightful sushi dinner with her one evening, followed by a pleasurable walk in Maruyama Park. The cherry blossom trees were in full bloom as they sauntered along. Without a doubt, this was the first time that he had fallen in love with someone (where the feeling was mutual); up to this point, he hadn't had a serious relationship back in the United States.

The next dinner that they had was at a Thai restaurant. As he was munching on his pad thai, Tomomi said, "I study TOEIC exam now. You help me?"

He had heard this exam mentioned a couple of times before in class, but he couldn't remember what the nature of this test was.

"What is the TOEIC exam?"

"It is test used in Japanese company. They look at score to help know English ability."

"I see. Well, your dinner lessons with me should certainly be helping you. Perhaps if I teach you more dirty words, then your score will go up."

She faintly smiled. Her expression indicated that she wanted to hear more willingness to help from him.

"Sure, I'll help you out with studying for this exam."

Internally, he felt a bit downcast about spending time with her studying for this exam; it didn't exactly sound like a deeply amorous way to enjoy her company. Possibly, if they were going to spend more time together and the exam preparation was a component of this, then that was more alluring than merely substituting some of the current intimacy for exam study. However, he certainly was not going to decline her request. He had found it meaningful to see her artwork, and therefore, it was quite reasonable to return the "favor" by lending a helping hand with this activity. An English teacher's job is never done, even in the bedroom with your girlfriend, he mused. This thought made him recall a joke that he had heard about marriage: "When I do something in the bedroom that my wife really likes, I'm talking about vacuuming." Well, in his case, instead of vacuuming, he mentored her on the TOEIC exam, in between cuddling and making out (which were probably less prevalent in long-term marriages). Kisses were so much more romantic in the context of TOEIC discussions.

Thomas learned that Tomomi was focusing on the TOEIC Speaking and Writing Test, which was one of two options. Pronunciation was assessed on this exam; he knew that this was often a challenge for Japanese speakers of English from his teaching experience. During one session, Tomomi was struggling to differentiate "f" and "v" sounds. Every time that she said "far", he kept hearing "var". *I sure hope that she can pronounce "fuck" correctly! That is the most important word in the English language!* Rain or shine, it appeared at the top of search queries on Google Scholar. Saying "vuck this exam" simply wasn't going to cut it; it was "fuck" or bust.

The "z" and "j" sounds also seemed to be formidable for her and many other Japanese speakers. What does Saul do when he discusses his culture in class? Do the students pronounce "Jew" like "zoo"? *Ouch. I'll be sure to avoid mentioning anything about Jews and zoos next time that I talk to Saul; he's probably quite fatigued of these images from his teaching here.* Saul most likely didn't anticipate that he would be back in Weimar-style Germany at times with errors that conflated Jews with the zoo.

He also spent a lot of time drilling Tomomi on difficult or unusual vocabulary words. The word "melancholy" came up on lists, for example. *Who says this word, other than in a Nathaniel Hawthorne novel?* "What's wrong? You're looking quite melancholy there!" Certainly, this word rarely came up in conversation. It did not seem to be a valuable use of time for Japanese students to spend loads of time studying it.

Shortly after Tomomi received her exam results, she phoned Thomas.

"I pass TOEIC exam. Thank you for your help."

"Excellent! What would you like to do this weekend? I miss you," he replied.

"I think I spend more time in art project now."

"So when would you like to meet again?"

"Maybe later. I do Ceramic now."

Here was the indirectness that Thomas despised. *If you want to break up with me, just tell me. I do not want to be involved with someone who bullshits in this manner. It's insulting to my sense of candor.*

He quivered with indignation. Somehow, he managed to utter, "Okay. I wish you the best of luck with your artwork."

Then he hung up. Later that evening, he informed Janek about what happened. Janek was measuring rice and about to start the rice cooker. He stopped dead in his tracks.

"Man, she was using you for English! She was cunning enough to wait a little bit before bringing up the TOEIC exam, but it's pretty suspicious that she ended it as soon as you weren't 'needed' for English any more. I'm sorry, dude. You're not the first gaijin to get conned for his English abilities in Japan. I've heard many other stories about this kind of thing. It happens the world over to overseas English teachers. Try not to take it too personally, even though that's easier said than done," he said.

The phone call still felt like a knife to his heart. He felt as if he were still on the phone with Tomomi, hearing those dreadful words from her. However, in the logical realm, Thomas was strongly inclined to agree with Janek's "analysis". Tomomi was one sly con artist. She had totally charmed him into thinking that she loved him with her endearing artwork sessions. Most likely, it was all part of a grand plan. There was a minute possibility that she had simply lost interest as the relationship had gone on, but the timing with the TOEIC exam was quite suspicious, as Janek said. Knowing that this often happened to English teachers did not lessen the pain of the breakup. He had developed feelings for her, especially compared to many of the girls whom he had gone to college with. She was a sweet, charming girl with stimulating interests.

Taking a step back, Thomas still viewed the whole experience as a good one overall. Sure, it had ended badly, but he had gained experience with women, and he had enjoyed the time that he spent with her, even if her motives were not pure. He recalled the quote that it was better to have loved and lost than never to have loved at all. It was all part of the human condition: every yin had its yang. These travel experiences often went hand in hand with awkwardness and discomfort. Likewise, romance often was accompanied by piercing pain and heartbreak. It was par for the course; the best course of action was to view it as part of a larger good experience rather than dwelling on the ending. Certainly a book can be great even if its ending is subpar; he would strive to view this former courtship in a similar light.

Moreover, as far as he knew, he still had the option of pursuing his love interest with Sendi after Japan. He decided to contact her again; writing to her would aid in forgetting about Tomomi. She responded a few days later, writing that she had found a position with a tech company in Tel Aviv. She wrote that the salary barely paid her expenses, but she was grateful to be gaining work experience. Finally, she added that when she witnessed a pale-skinned man on the beach who was quite sunburned, that had reminded her of Thomas. *Thank you, Indiana clouds, for my ghostlike skin.*

He was now beginning to enter the last few months of his teaching contract. If the relationship with Tomomi had continued to flower, then he likely would have needed to sign another year contract in Japan. The fact also remained that he still had not sojourned to Tokyo. He had developed a deep appreciation for the old capital of Kyoto, but he had not seen the new capital. In some respects, he was living in the past in Kyoto. A country's capital is often the center of the action; it was a bit different in the United States since it is such a large country. American action seemed to be equally split between the three centers of New York (finance),

DC (politics), and Los Angeles (entertainment) in many respects. But in Japan, all three of these aspects were heavily concentrated in Tokyo, not Kyoto. Kyoto was much more of a historical city in the context of twenty-first-century Japan.

He decided to spend a lengthy weekend there of three days. He would take the bullet train there to minimize the travel time, even though it was quite costly. The financial damage was $250 round trip. The overnight bus, on the other hand, was a screaming bargain at $150 (round trip). He believed that it was well worth spending the extra $100 to save time; an overnight bus would be more appropriate if he were taking an extended trip in Japan and was not tied down by a work schedule.

Furthermore, there was something to be said as well for "experiencing" the shinkansen. The bullet train was a marvel of Japanese technological know-how. This would be a good segue into the "new Japan" world of Tokyo. It had been immensely rewarding to explore the Buddhist temples and (you saved $200 by switching to) geiko district of Kyoto, but this did not represent all of Japan. No, Japan was a complex, poly-headed monster, and these Kyoto frolics only represented a couple of the heads, at most. There was much more to this beast than exclusively Kyoto. Therefore, merely performing a financial cost analysis of the shinkansen vs. the overnight bus was missing the big picture. Foreign travel wasn't mostly about money. If saving money is a person's highest prerogative, then he or she would not do *any* foreign travel since it inevitably is a costly undertaking. Foreign travel was about experiences, the mind, the soul, and the (heavily exhausted) body.

As he entered the shinkansen, he saw that organization and cleanliness were once again the order of the day. The "hai, dozo" man would have been in his element here. As a subject, it was certainly not fertile ground for a modernist, cluttered painting. Thomas was impressed by its outer appearance: ultra-sleek and modern looking. The very front of the train had a somewhat "amphibious" appearance; it seemed as if the train was capable of detaching from the tracks and then plunging head first into the water, safely carrying passengers through the sea. On the other hand, it also seemed capable of actions similar to the DeLorean in *Back to the Future Part II*, as if it would disengage from the tracks and catapult into the air as a flying machine. Amphibious was the perfect word for this organism; it appeared to be capable of anything.

Just as he understood the French's pride in their food, he also believed that the Japanese had quite legitimate reasons to be very proud of their technology. *Did this justify them looking down at me and checking to make sure that I didn't steal anything? Probably not; the incident in Kyoto was prejudice, plain and simple. But nonetheless, Japanese technology was superb. It is an undeniable reality that the United States doesn't have trains that measure up to these ones.* Was this an apples and apples comparison? Most likely not, since Japan was extremely densely populated compared to the United States. The sprawling character of America strongly inhibited the development of a robust train system, as did the cheap cost of gas and driving in general.

But the fact that it was an apples and oranges comparison did not detract from the stateliness of this amphibious train. Yes, this train was fit for Hirohito or any king in history and now he, Thomas Gephardt, talking monkey, was riding on this superorganism along with the plentiful number of well-dressed business travelers on the train. He still saw very few wrinkles on the clothing of the passengers. *I probably have more wrinkles on my clothes than the rest of the passengers in this train car combined.*

He had heard that "appearance is everything" in Asia and this certainly seemed to apply to Japan. Surface appearances were extremely important. People seemed to mostly hide their inner minds out in public anyway; this only heightened the importance of surface impressions, or the outer mind.

After he exited the bullet train, he looked for the nearest subway station. Hordes of people walked past him, in a rush to reach their destinations. *They seem less friendly than the people in Kyoto. They are even more distant, and less relaxed.* As he scrutinized the panorama of the surrounding area, it was clear as a bell that he was encircled by skyscrapers and office buildings. Traditional temples here were an endangered species compared to their ubiquity in Kyoto. This was the new Japan. Tokyo had only been the capital since 1868; before it was the capital, it was called Edo.

When Thomas was on the train, he had decided against staying in a youth hostel in Tokyo. He didn't have a burning desire to meet other travelers today. His teaching program had provided ample opportunity to rub shoulders with fellow gaijin, and a private room seemed to have more appeal than sleeping on a bunk bed in another crowded room. He hadn't forgotten Ron, the Aussie traveler who had originally recommended Japan to him. Indeed, they had met in a youth hostel. But his mood tonight simply did not fit the youth hostel environment. Instead, he took the subway to a ryokan, or traditional Japanese inn. As he expected, his room was filled with wooden furniture and a bed resembling a sleeping bag. Traditionally, the Japanese slept on the floor on a soft mattress; Western-style beds came much later. The ryokan gave foreign travelers the opportunity to experience a more traditional Japanese environment, even while they were in the hectic metropolis of Tokyo.

The next day, he set out for Harajuku. Harajuku was known as a spot that was full of youth culture and fashion trends. He figured that this would be one locality in the city that should epitomize aspects of the new Japan. The Japanese youngsters here had dyed hair in a diverse array of colors, much more akin to a rainbow, compared to the monochromatic spectrum that he'd seen on the shinkansen. One teen had a pink tie draped over his t-shirt. There were many black leather jackets, trench coats, and facial piercings. Some of the girls had long pigtails. *All that they're missing are guitars, amplifiers, and a stage.* Without a doubt, he felt hundreds of miles away from the Buddhist temples of Kyoto. This was a good counterbalance to the conservatism of most Japanese dress, which was heavily influenced by the corporate world.

Countercultures seemed to flourish the most in very large urban areas, and this was no exception to that trend. The Greater Tokyo Area was the largest metropolitan area in the world with a population of almost forty million. With a population that enormous, it was not possible to ferret out all non-conformity and rebellion. This kind of size simply allowed for too much possibility for diversity; Harajuku was one notable example.

Soon he hopped on a very crowded Tokyo subway train and visited Tsukiji Fish Market. The Tokyo subway was so packed that some men were employed to push people onto the trains (while stationary) to maximize occupancy. He had never seen this level of population density before. Japan was crowded in general, but Tokyo took this trend to a whole new level. *I should tell these dudes that they are being very pushy. If they understand me, they will simply nod and assert that this is their job.* Apparently sometimes pushiness was needed for urban efficiency; possibly many people in other large cities such as New York City would agree with this. In general, he found the Japanese to be in the extreme opposite direction of pushiness with their formality and politeness. Therefore, in some respects, these push men were every bit as countercultural as the youths in Harajuku, though from a different frame of reference.

Tsukiji Fish Market was an enormous wholesale Japanese seafood market (in the inner market). Here, fish were processed and auctioned off to merchants. He saw enormous tuna, shrimp, prawns, octopus, sardines, caviar, and numerous other types of seafood. In the outer market, it was possible to buy a bevy of goods. A mix of wholesale shops and retail shops sold fresh seafood, fresh produce, and other food-and-kitchen items, such as spatulas and measuring cups. Additionally, he saw many sushi restaurants, which one would expect. The fish had a very short trip from wholesaler to restaurant plate in this area. Instead of "farm to table", this place was "sea to table."

The wholesale fish market was another example of "geography is destiny". Japan's close proximity to the water resulted in an enormous seafood industry. Landlocked countries simply could not compete with Japan's water resources in this area. It was almost as if the Japanese were destined to "invent" sushi due to their geography. Island geography was very conducive to a diet of raw fish.

After spending another comforting, peaceful night in a ryokan, the next day, he headed over to Ginza. Ginza was a luxurious shopping district in Tokyo; he had read that it was one of the world's most luxurious shopping areas. The department stores seemed to have a boundless height. *If these stores were anthropomorphic, they would be a formidable match for Godzilla. Certainly falling out of the top floor would be quite dangerous!* This was another shining example of the new Japan. This type of opulence would feel out of place in the traditional streets of

Kyoto, without a doubt. It would be the equivalent of the Sesame Street skits where children are asked, "What doesn't belong in this picture?" Ginza was a self-evident consequence of Japan's rapid economic growth and industrialization during the modern period. The old, feudal Japan simply didn't have the resources or wealth to support this kind of luxury.

Japan was clearly a "shopping-oriented" society; it shared this trait with the United States. Thomas would not call France extremely "shopping-oriented" in the same sense. High fashion was clearly popular in France, but the French didn't seem to have the same "drive" to consume things in the same way. The small portions in French restaurants were a good metaphor for their shopping habits; they preferred to consume in smaller doses. Japan also had small portions in its restaurants, so this was no guarantee of a limited shopping culture. The Japanese were not huge eaters, but when it came to non-food items, there was a stronger urge to consume, he believed. His jaw dropped when he saw such small girls walking around the area with so many bags on their arms. Possibly the bags were full of the myriad cosmetics that he had seen on the women's faces on his plane ride. *This was how one wore a Kafka mask—one shopped in Ginza.*

It was an aspect of Japanese society that he did not find appealing; he thought that it was wasteful to "over-shop". He strongly preferred buying what he needed, rather than accumulating large piles of material goods. He had heard an expression before along the lines of "I'd rather have a passport full of stamps than a house full of stuff." Thomas could not agree more. The memories from foreign travel lasted a lifetime; it was hard to argue the same value about merely buying a shirt, pair of jeans, or earrings. These goods were merely needed to sustain life rather than give a deeper meaning to the human condition. *Robin Williams in* Dead

<u>Poets Society</u> *would not argue that these goods "suck all the marrow out of life". No, in fact, too much consumption sucked all the marrow out of the human soul. Thoreau would be rolling over in his grave.*

It did not seem to be the case that it was inevitable that strong economic growth led to overconsumption since he had not felt this ethos in France (or England during his limited time there). No, something else drove this behavior. It was indisputably related to values, but what caused these kinds of values to develop? Was it because of the French intellectualism that they were less into material goods? This was the most palatable armchair explanation that he was able to offer. He believed that there was a correlation between intellectualism and reduced interest in shopping; it was difficult to envision material goods strongly impressing intellectuals in the same way. Few poets extolled the virtues of rampant consumption in their works; excess shopping lacked "artsy" value.

He preferred to leave Tokyo on a higher note than having a sour taste from witnessing excess shopping. Therefore, he spent the rest of the day at Ueno Park. Japan was highly consumer-oriented, but they had also demonstrated a strong appreciation for nature with the copious beautiful gardens and parks. Ueno Park was quite spacious and he had read that it was one of the country's first parks. The park had over 8,800 trees. More notably, it had eight hundred cherry trees and it was especially famous for cherry blossom trees during the spring. Furthermore, the park contained Shinobazu Pond, which was a significant wintering ground for birds. Various species of ducks were in the area during the winter months.

Did these parks appeal to different sectors of Japanese society than the shopping? Or was it possible to love both consumption and nature? It was certainly possible in theory, but it seemed contradictory. On the other hand, there were an inordinate number of things about Japan that he did not understand, so it was certainly possible that this was part of the convoluted maze that he felt walking through Japan. However, taking a stab in the dark, he guessed that it did appeal to a different sector of Japanese society. It was a homogenous culture, but not completely uniform. There was still cultural diversity in its midst.

There were elements of the older Japan, as well, in this park. Part of the park had a shrine to Benzaiten, the Buddhist goddess of fortune. He researched on his phone that Benzaiten was originally derived from a Hindu goddess, Saraswati; Saraswati is mentioned in the Rig-Veda, which was an ancient collection of Indian Sanskrit hymns. Japan was somewhat isolated from its Asian neighbors since it was an island, and this had undoubtedly contributed to its highly unique character. But clearly, Japan could not escape all Asian currents. Buddhism, which originated on the Indian subcontinent, had managed to permeate parts of Japanese society; this was a strong river that Japan had been unable to avoid, merely from being an island.

After returning to Kyoto, Thomas had one main item left on his to-do list before he left Japan in a few months: he had not yet been to a porn vending machine. This was a uniquely Japanese phenomenon. Japan was saturated with vending machines, and these machines contained a manifold number of items. This fact, combined with Japan's perverse sexual culture, made the porn machines a near certainty. He was not surprised that there was a large porn industry in Japan. The extreme formality and politeness repressed so much human instinct. It was only natural that the Japanese needed to release these repressed feelings in some way, and pornography seemed to be a logical outlet for doing so. Another more global factor most likely contributed to high porn usage among the male population as well: the lower status of women.

Congratulations, Japan. You possibly have the most perverts per capita anywhere in the world! What a ringing endorsement for extreme politeness. Though politeness and perversion start with the same letter, who knew that there might be some kind of link between the two of them? His revulsion towards Japanese politeness was consistent with his strong belief in the Aristotelian middle or moderation in general. This was yet another reason to push moderation; potentially, it reduced perversion in the population.

Porn was undoubtedly another feature of the new Japan as well; he highly doubted that the ancient Shinto priests were into pornography if they were consistent with their moral teachings. Though based on the perverse behavior of many Catholic priests, this was not necessarily a safe assumption. Possibly porn was part of both the old and the new Japan?

Since his roommate Albert was highly into porn, he decided to go with him one night to one of the porn vending machines that were near their apartment. As they looked at the machine, Albert said, "Some of these magazines overlap with Japanese anime. There's not an exact boundary here between anime and porn."

"You're the expert, Albert."

"Hell yeah. The reason we're here at night is because I didn't want the Japanese to see a couple of gaijin dudes gawking at this porn here during the day. I still haven't adapted to the whole gaijin existence here. Back home, I'm a person. Here, I'm a freak!"

"I know what you're saying. I think, though, I've accustomed myself for the most part now to being a racial minority. I was quite annoyed when I was profiled in the geisha area, but other than that, I haven't had too many traumatic experiences outside of not understanding the culture very well."

"Oh, we're never going to understand the culture here. This is an experience for sure, but not one of cultural understanding."

"Yes, I agree, Albert. I think that I'm going to travel to Israel next. I'm not quite ready to head back to Indiana just yet, and I have a 'nice-looking contact' there."

"You should talk to Saul before we are done. He knows a fair amount about Israel."

"I think that's a great suggestion. Let's arrange to have lunch soon."

"Will do. I hope that you enjoyed your porn machine experience" Albert said, chuckling.

"I will definitely never forget it. I don't think that I'm going to be able to check out a vending machine like this anywhere else in the world."

"Hell yeah! Japanese vending machines are badass, man."

And with this inspiring thought, under the cover of night, Batman and Robin fled the porn vending machine and returned to their apartment.

A week later, Albert kept his word and arranged for a lunch with the three of them at a traditional Japanese restaurant. Thomas ordered the tonkatsu. It had been a few months since he had eaten this dish, and therefore, he had a craving for it. He never would have guessed that at some point in his life, he would "crave" Japanese food, but now that he had been in the country for several months, some of the food had certainly grown on him. Hence, he had some cravings as if he were a quasi-native. Albert ordered tempura; he loved fried food after spending many years in Houston. Houston was close to Louisiana and hence adopted the "southern fried" influence of its neighbor. Saul noted that he was not particularly hungry and consequently ordered udon noodles. Thomas was not a noodles aficionado; he felt far too hungry after eating noodles. *What is the point of eating something if you feel so hungry relatively soon? These noodle dishes are more suitable for a light snack than a full meal.*

"Saul, I only have a couple of months left in Japan. I think that I will work in Israel next."

"So you're definitely not returning to the U.S. for a bit? You don't miss your family at all?" he said.

Feeling a modicum of guilt, he replied, "We've never been a particularly tight-knit family. I don't disavow my parents, but I am not ready to return to Indiana yet. I want to experience one more place and be able to claim a holy trinity of travel experiences."

"Yes, things are often nice in threes; it gives you a beginning, middle, and end. How would you rate your experience in Japan?"

"It is a unique land and the history is fascinating, but I find the culture to be far too formal and polite. I feel too much of a wall with the people here; it seems to be very difficult to get to know most of them. That expression about the Japanese having a rose on the outside and a knife on the inside really seems to ring true in my experiences. I never know what people are thinking."

Saul nodded a couple of times and placed down his Sapporo beer bottle. "Thomas, then Israel might be the ideal change for you. It is the extreme opposite of Japan. Are you looking for the other extreme?"

"It could be a quite refreshing change."

"I'm Jewish, and we're known for being direct and often confrontational, but the Israelis take it to a whole new level. You could say that Israel is Jews on steroids, and many of the guys are quite buff, so some of them might be on steroids anyway. You always know what's on their mind. I guarantee you that you will not have that issue if you go there."

Thomas smiled and felt fired up. "That sounds intriguing, Saul. That is also in a different part of the world than both France and Japan. I think that this could be a fulfilling completion to my non-Roman triumvirate."

Albert's countenance lost a lot of enthusiasm when the subject of Israel came up. "I sure as hell am not going there. They have a lot of religious fanatics over there and sometimes terrorist bombings. Fuck that shit," he said.

Saul seems to have heard this viewpoint many times before. It's almost as if he were expecting Albert to make this remark. His facial expressions and posture are completely unchanged after hearing this comment. Saul replied calmly, "It's not the safest country in the world, for sure. But the probability that you will die from a terrorist attack is extremely small. There is very little street crime, so other than the terrorist threat, it is a quite safe country. The U.S. has religious fanatics as well; Israel does not have a monopoly on that."

"Yeah, and a lot of the Christian fanatics in the U.S. are militantly pro-Israel since the Bible is based there," Albert replied.

"I'm with your line of reasoning, Saul," said Thomas. "There is some risk anywhere that you go, and I love history. Israel and the wider region must be overflowing with history."

Saul grinned, looking honored. "Amen to that, Thomas. You will have endless possibilities for historical exploration in Israel. You need to figure out what you're going to do there though."

"Yes, I will research work programs in Israel. If I can find something suitable, then I will embark there for my next adventure. My female crush may have some suggestions as well, ha ha."

Saul and Albert smiled knowingly.

As Thomas did his research, he found one program that was quite common for non-Jews: working on a kibbutz. A kibbutz was defined as some kind of communal settlement, and usually it was a farm. *This would be a good antidote to the crass consumerism of Ginza. I can become some hipster working on a pinko cooperative. If I ever want to run for office in America as a "socialist", then this should help burnish my credentials. Republicans will accuse me of a Communist plot to ruin the country since I shared resources on a communal farm. However, most Republicans are staunchly pro-Israel, so which one of their loyalties would take preference: their militant support of Israel, or their abhorrence of "socialism"? I will only be able to answer this question if I run for office, which would be quite an undertaking; I do not know if I have the stamina for this endeavor. But I'll never know if I refrain from running for office.*

From his research, he learned that he would need to apply for a volunteer visa, and if he were accepted to the program, he would receive a small stipend. Saul had previously mentioned that Israel had a very high cost of living (similar to Japan in this regard), so he would need to live frugally during his kibbutz time and draw upon some of his savings from teaching English. The experience would last for a few months. Free housing, meals, and social activities were also provided as part of the package.

This certainly will not be economically lucrative, even less so than teaching here. But it would be a unique experience, and that is the ultimate motivation for foreign travel, not financial rewards. Foreign travel is all about the soul, not the pocket book.

He decided that he would submit his application materials. There were few other options for non-Jews in Israel. His research confirmed this, and when he consulted with Saul about this question, Saul agreed that this was the best option. English teaching opportunities in Israel seemed to be more limited and required more certifications; Saul believed that the Israelis were more comfortable speaking English due to the nature of their education system. Class participation was much more heavily encouraged in Israel compared to Japan; therefore, the students did not have the same levels of hesitation about speaking another language.

"Since Israel is the extreme opposite of Japan, it should be no surprise that Israeli students have no difficulties expressing their opinions," Saul said with a wide grin.

"Also, don't expect to receive these opinions at what we consider to be a 'normal' volume. There is a lot of yelling and shouting in this area of the world; throw away expectations of the East Asian diplomatic tone of speaking, if you are going to adapt to the environment over there," he added.

Once again, Thomas considered it fortunate that he had met Sendi to point him in the direction of Israel, just as it had been fortuitous that Ron the Aussie traveler had steered him towards Japan. Foreign travelers tended to be interesting people with thought-provoking ideas. Their willingness to leave their borders and enrich themselves with novel (or poetic) experiences caused them to become more engaging people.

A couple of months later, Thomas received good news. He had been accepted to work on a kibbutz. He was assigned to the kibbutz Neve Eitan, in northern Israel, in the Beit She'an valley. He was clueless regarding how to pronounce "Neve"; was it a short or long "e"? In some senses, traveling to the far corners of the world meant continually starting over again. He was now quite familiar with Japanese pronunciation after ten months, though certainly not fluent in the language. Now he would be attempting to master new sounds once again in another foreign alphabet.

Saul had previously demonstrated a few Hebrew words to him; it sounded like a much more "throat-oriented" language compared to Japanese or English. Saul had also mentioned that its linguistic (and geographical) neighbor Arabic also contained a lot of similar "throat" type of sounds. *Well, at least it's softer than German. This language sounds akin to mild spitting at times, while German is the real McCoy and they spit full throttle.*

It now seemed wise to get back in touch with Sendi about his move to Israel. That day, Thomas emailed her:

"Sendi,

How are you? I haven't erased you from my memory. That would be quite a feat, since you are one of the most gorgeous women that I've ever seen in my time here on this planet. I have big news: I will be coming to Israel to volunteer on a kibbutz! It seemed to be the best option available to a non-Jew. The kibbutz is called Neve Eitan in the north. Are you familiar with it? I hope that we can meet up soon after my arrival, and you can show me your intriguing culture. How is your life since we last spoke?

See you soon,

Thomas"

Sendi took five days to reply to him; Thomas did not know how to interpret this interval of time. It had been a long time since they had spoken, and they had only met once. He could not expect that he would remain fresh in her memory indefinitely. At last she responded:

"Shalom Thomas,

You will need to become familiar this word soon :). I am forget so much English now. I spoke English more in Paris compared now. I hear the man calling me gorgeous a lot outside of Israel, but here I am just more normal :). You will see many beautiful women here. I look for other job now. My boss give me much stress, but I learn every day. Contact me when you are in Israel. I hope that you have good stay at kibbutz. I do not know this kibbutz. I cannot know it all about my country. There is so much! You will be amazed how much we have in small space. The cultural density is high here; I hope this make sense in English. Have safe flight to the holy land.

Sendi"

He took a deep breath and exhaled slowly. Yes, there was some momentary relief that she had eventually responded, but he was a bit puzzled by her comment about him seeing many beautiful women in Israel. Was this her "feminine" way of telling him that she didn't still have as strong of an interest in him? On the other hand, it was unrealistic to expect that a girl who hadn't seen him in months would still be fawning over him. Human lust simply didn't work that way. He believed that the best approach was to enter Israel with minimal expectations about Sendi and focus more holistically on the country instead of her. He had already been damaged enough emotionally from the split with Tomomi; he didn't need another tsunami-sized wipeout inside the chambers of his heart.

During the next six weeks, he wrapped up his teaching in Japan. He said his goodbyes to many of the other teachers and pledged to keep in touch, primarily through Facebook. His tenure as a talking monkey had now come to an end; work on the kibbutz would involve far less talking. Would he be completely losing his monkey identity, or could he be thought of as a "walking monkey" in Israel? The year in Japan had been a very stimulating experience, but his mind was now fully focused on the next adventure.

6

Chapter Six

November 2016

He decided to pay a bit extra to fly on the Israeli airline El Al. It was $500 more expensive than Turkish Airlines, but he believed that he would get a "head start" on his glimpse into the culture by flying on an Israeli airline. He liked their motto: "It's not just an airline. It's Israel." Total flying time would be about twenty hours. There were cheaper options with two stops, but he decided that it was worthwhile paying extra for one stop. World travel is fabulous, but spending heaps of time (as the Aussies would say) at the airport is not so praiseworthy. He still hadn't fully recovered from the "hai, dozo" man at the Osaka airport; he hoped that there would be no reincarnation of this man on his trip to Tel Aviv. There had been enough traumas from too much formalism in Japan for a few lifetimes.

On the flight, not staring at the Israeli female passengers was easier said than done. Sendi was unquestionably on the mark about this feature of the Israeli landscape. These women were definitely even more beautiful than the women in France. Most of them had very attractive olive skin; he found it to be near perfection. The Israelis spoke in animated tones; the Great Wall of Inhibition that he had found in Japan seemed to have come tumbling down, never to be put back together again.

A couple of times in the aisle, people pushed past him and said nothing. As an American and certainly after a year in Japan, Thomas was very accustomed to hearing "excuse me". This shift in cultural mores would be one aspect of life that he would need to acclimate himself to in this new land.

Yes, they seemed to be on the pushy side, literally and figuratively. What you see is what you get with these people. Saul wasn't being ironic when he said that they were the extreme opposite of the Japanese. If the Japanese were snow, Israelis were rain. If the Japanese were summer, Israelis were winter. This was an opposite, clashing universe that he was entering. It would be no easy feat to imagine a conversation between an Israeli and a Japanese person; most likely, the Japanese person would become offended very quickly and the Israeli would get very frustrated that his or her Japanese counterpart was "beating around the bush" too much and not getting right down to the point. A Martian could probably communicate better with the Japanese than the Israelis.

He was served a meal of chicken shawarma with hummus. A cucumber and tomato salad was served on the side, along with very fresh bread. If he were a "food critic" for this meal, then his review would definitely be two thumbs up. For a few minutes, all of his concerns and worries fell away; when he tasted this food, he was somewhere else, in another realm. It all tasted extremely fresh. He doubted that there was one molecule of chemicals in the food. This was very clean food, as in the "pre-industrial" days. Saul had mentioned to him not to expect

"Jewish deli"-style food in Israel; this food was from Eastern European Jewish culture. Israeli food, on the other hand, was much closer to Arabic food. Therefore, it was no surprise that he was served chicken shawarma with hummus.

Internally, Thomas was clear-headed. If his emotional chemistry at this moment were a music playlist, it was "yoga music" on this flight, compared to the last two big international flights. Each long flight seemed to become a little bit more "elementary, my dear Watson" to deal with. His psyche on the flight to France had been akin to a turbulent storm, and now, he was almost beginning to feel like a "professional" traveler. *I can do this. I survived staying with a French host family and teaching for an entire year in Japan. If I can handle one year of teaching in Japan, I can definitely tough it out through this.* Travel experience was giving him more confidence about his possibilities. Surviving one "mission" made him feel as if he could persevere through another one. His gut feeling was that Israel would require less adjustment than Japan. First, he would not be a racial minority any more. Second, it was arguably more influenced by Western culture than Japan. Third, he strongly preferred the Israeli bluntness to the Japanese opaqueness. He would have far less frustration trying to figure out what people meant when they interacted with him in Israel.

As he continued to mull over his future adventures, he fell into a deep sleep for several hours. When he woke up, the plane was close to landing in Tel Aviv. As he walked off the plane, security personnel were omnipresent. *It felt like a dream when I had my shawarma and hummus, but now, in all directions, I feel scrutiny from the security presence. Time to wake up!* He trailed behind a darker-skinned man who looked Arab; as soon as this man was off the plane, a tough-looking security man said to him,

"Passport!" Once again, he saw that people got right down to the point when communicating.

Thomas, since he did not look Arab or Muslim, did not have to produce his passport just yet. He realized that the Israelis did not try to hide at all that they profiled people based on appearance. It wasn't akin to an American airport where the security screeners spent as much time with an eighty-year-old grandmother as they did with young men, in an effort to appear to be "objective". *I would definitely feel less welcome here if I looked Arab. This is not an "open society" in the same regard as the United States.* It did seem to be a waste of resources to heavily screen eighty-year-old grandmothers, but he could also see the American point of view; there was some merit in attempting to at least give the veneer of a welcoming society. He had felt completely humiliated when he was profiled in Kyoto, and he did not wish these experiences on others. *Profiling definitely makes one feel subhuman. Since I seem to "blend in" better here, it is less probable that I will be profiled in this setting.*

After escaping the experience of being openly profiled, he proceeded to the official immigration counter for foreign citizens. Here was where the official "interrogation" began. The immigration agent was a middle-aged balding man who wore a skullcap. He would later learn that this word was "yarmulke" in Yiddish and "kippah" in Hebrew. There was no "welcome to Israel" greeting; this was ultra-serious business. The man immediately scanned his passport and checked the photograph against his appearance in person.

"How long you stay in Israel?" he asked in a thick Israeli accent.

"Three months."

"What will you do for three months?"

"Volunteer work on a kibbutz."

"Do you have papers from the kibbutz?"

"Yes." He then proceeded to hand over his acceptance papers.

"Where is the kibbutz?"

Fortunately, Thomas still remembered after he had handed over the papers. He felt as though he were being examined rather rigorously.

"Neve Eitan," he said hesitantly, as he was unfamiliar with the pronunciation.

The official immediately corrected his poor Hebrew pronunciation. "Neve *Eitan*, yes."

The man furrowed his brows a bit more after hearing the bad Hebrew. "Why are you volunteering on kibbutz?"

"Because I want to experience Israel, and I have few options since I am not Jewish."

"What do you do after the three months finish?"

"I will most likely return to the United States."

"Do you have enough funds for living in Israel for three months?"

"I have some money saved from teaching in Japan."

"No more questions." The man then stamped his passport. Thomas had heard that some people asked the officials in Israel not to stamp their passports since this then prevented them from traveling to many Muslim countries. Thomas, however, had no existing plans to visit any Muslim countries in the near future. After this quite extended period of travel, he planned to spend some time back in the United States before undertaking any further international travel.

This "examination" was certainly more thorough than his entrance interviews in France and Japan. He realized, however, that Israel had a quite precarious security situation in its "neighborhood"; therefore, he was not surprised that the interview was more detailed. Japan was fortunate enough to be quite isolated on its own island. Unlike Israel, it was not landlocked among numerous hostile countries.

Now it was time to search for his arranged transfer. This too was almost beginning to feel like a quasi-routine; this was now the third time in as many countries that a foreign person would be picking him up at the airport. It wasn't enormously difficult to locate his name among the signs; many of the signs had Hebrew writing, which obviously excluded him from consideration. A well-dressed man in black pants and a blue shirt was holding a sign with his name; this man had no skullcap. Thomas had learned from Saul that more liberal Jews did not wear the skullcap on a daily basis. Saul had mentioned that a large percentage of liberal Jews did not practice the religion at all and mainly focused on the cultural aspects of Judaism.

"Hello, I am Yosi. I will drive you to the kibbutz. Can I take a bag?"

"Thank you, Yosi. My bags are not very heavy; I can carry them."

Thomas noticed that Yosi had not given his last name. In both France and Japan, the men had given both their first name and their last name when introducing themselves at the airport. He believed that, most likely, this demonstrated that Israel was less formal than France or Japan.

Yosi's demeanor emanated quite a bit of warmth, especially compared to his airport drivers in the previous two countries. With Paul, he felt that it had taken some time to break the ice. Eventually, Paul opened up to him, but in the beginning, he came across as very distant. In Japan, on the other hand, he had never perceived any closeness with people. Jerry, one teacher whom he had worked with, had been living in Japan for seven years and had said that it had taken four years before he had developed any meaningful relationships with the people there, so Thomas was certainly not alone in feeling sizable barriers with the natives. Even though Yosi did not speak much English, he was quite friendly; he was by far the most approachable of his three airport drivers. His facial expressions were certainly much more "radiant looking" compared to Paul and Hiroto, his Japanese counterpart. Thomas believed that the sunny weather in Israel certainly helped in this regard.

The drive to the kibbutz took approximately ninety minutes. Yosi's driving style was much more similar to Paul's than Hiroto's. Hiroto had been an extremely cautious driver. Yosi, on the other hand, emulated Paul's more kamikaze-like style of accelerating hard on the gas pedal; it was a bit ironic that the French and Israeli drivers were much more kamikaze-like than the Japanese one. Yosi also had no qualms about driving in a bus lane for fifteen minutes. He was not unique on the highway; many of the cars were driving quite fast and there seemed to be very little courtesy between drivers. There seemed to be a continuum between the passengers on the airplane who pushed past him abruptly and the Israeli drivers on this highway. Fighting for space on the airplane had merely been replaced with struggling for space on the road.

Thomas had known before coming to Israel that it was a quite tiny country; it was now unmistakable that space was limited here. The density of cars ensured that Israel had a very crowded feeling; this was one aspect in which Israel was quite similar to Japan. He highly doubted that he would find many others. Other than this superficial similarity, overall, Israel seemed to be in a different galaxy compared to Japan.

When he arrived at the kibbutz, it did not match the image

that he had expected in his mind. He had assumed that it would resemble a small, intimate commune. Instead, it was a sprawling agricultural complex. Clearly, not all of the labor was manual; there were many heavy machines at work. Perhaps the smaller commune was from an older era, he considered. This contrast demonstrated another valuable aspect of the travel experience. Mental preconceptions often strongly conflicted with physical reality. The primary means of discovering that these mental preconceptions were flawed was to experience the physical reality; otherwise, these "prejudices" would remain. Reading books also aided in dispelling preconceived notions, but this did not "smack a person in the face" in the same way as eyewitness accounts. Reading still heavily relied on the imagination, while firsthand observation forced a person to confront his mental images in a much more formidable manner.

He was tempted to ask about the mechanization on the kibbutz, but Yosi seemed to have quite limited English. Yosi dropped him off in a building that resembled a dormitory. There were hallways of many small rooms, and Yosi escorted him to his room and handed him some information in English about the next day's activities. He would have a new volunteers' group meeting tomorrow afternoon.

The room was small, but nicely furnished with a bed, a small reading chair, and a desk. He decided to explore the kibbutz. He found his way to a large cafeteria with an attached bar. He knew that he would be eating his meals in the cafeteria; he had been informed that meals were provided in his pre-arrival materials. Many people were eating together in the cafeteria. *Olives, hummus, fresh fruits and vegetables. It looks extremely fresh and delicious. Food here is beautiful, plain and simple.* It was a challenge to resist eating from the "buffet" until tomorrow.

Thomas was beginning to wonder if Israel would turn out to be a greater food paradise than France. Much less butter was used in the food here; possibly, the food would be equally as delicious and healthier as well. However, it remained to be seen if the variety of food in Israel would be as considerable compared to France.

He also was able to find a small swimming pool and a few tennis courts. There was potential here for a quite vigorous community spirit. The presence of mere agricultural machinery would not prevent this development, in and of itself. This kibbutz was not a "tiny commune" physically, but it still could be quite collectivist spiritually. In the cafeteria, people were highly engaged in their conversations. Most of the tables had large groups as well. It was undeniable that he would be giving up quite a bit of privacy on the kibbutz; the bathroom was communal in addition to the kitchen. However, he had rarely felt as though he were a member of any type of strong community in the past. The possibility for a powerful community ethos could be quite empowering and add a pleasant layer to his foreign travel experiences. In Japan, the teachers in his program shared common experiences, but they were scattered among many different schools. The geographical diffusion prevented the formation of a strong communal feeling. Occasionally, they would gather in large groups for social events, but these events did not occur with enough frequency to preserve a communal feeling.

As much as he would have enjoyed continuing to ponder communitarianism vs. privacy, it was unmistakable that he was exhausted by the extremely lengthy flight from Japan. It was now wise to rest his tired mind and body so that he would be able to fully absorb the meeting tomorrow; he was going to be learning a lot of vital information about the next few months.

At the afternoon meeting the next day, there was a group of eight new volunteers, including Thomas. The other volunteers were from Canada, Germany, Brazil, Greece, Australia (two people), and Malaysia. All of them spoke a good amount of English. Most of the volunteers, like Thomas, were under thirty, but the man from Malaysia was elderly and retired. Thomas thought that possibly it was easier for the Malaysian man to obtain approval since he was older. Although Malaysia was not an arch-enemy of Israel, he figured that the Israeli immigration services would have higher suspicions of applicants from Muslim countries, just as the people at the airport who either were Arab or appeared to be Arab were screened and examined much more heavily.

Ehud, the volunteer coordinator at the kibbutz, extensively discussed the kibbutz routine. They would be working for eight to nine hours a day in various tasks. Their responsibilities would be changed every month in order to provide a more multifarious experience. Ehud said that he was elated that they had chosen to spend time volunteering in Israel. "In media, you see many images of Israel, and they are not always correct. I hope that in this time, you will have more full viewpoint of this place," he said.

Thomas learned that his first job would be picking dates (the fruit, not women) and plums. His hours would be between 6:00 a.m. and 4:30 p.m. with an hour break for lunch. Clearly, he would be waking up much earlier here compared to Japan; his earliest class in Japan began at 8:30 a.m. *I better learn to become a morning spirit here or this will be a very prolonged three months. However, foreign travel should be about maximizing character-building experiences. The mind should be stretched in as many dimensions as possible. Learning to adapt to a particularly early*

work schedule will be yet another character-expanding experience.
The Israelis were proud of this land that they had "occupied" (which was a somewhat loaded term within the context of the current conflict) for thousands of years. Ehud's manner of speaking was a legacy of this pride. He gave a history of the kibbutz and there was no doubt that he believed that agriculture was practiced at a cutting-edge level in Israel, both in general and with regard to this specific location. They were proud of how much they had developed the land into an advanced economy, and now he had an opportunity to share in the continuation of this development through diligent, hard labor on the land. Certainly this communal farming ethos was not present everywhere in the world, and the Israelis had their own distinct flavor to contribute. He hoped to learn much from imbibing this flavor.

Ehud also discussed the frequent optional social activities. The kibbutz had a bar for evening socializing, the pool, and also some planned social events. Thomas also learned that he was given one week off during the three-month period; the kibbutz encouraged volunteers to travel around Israel during this period; unquestionably, he would be doing an excursion to Tel Aviv and Jerusalem. "We do not want you think that all Israelis work on farms," Ehud noted with a large grin.

I do not think that you need to be concerned about that. I have yet to encounter that stereotype of the Israelis. Most likely, he was just attempting to be humorous, but it would speak quite poorly of these volunteers if we extrapolated about all of Israel based on the observations of one kibbutz. Surely we world travelers here have more sophisticated powers of analysis than this. In fact, Thomas ventured to guess that farming was one of the last images that came into the minds of most outsiders when imagining the Israelis. Regardless, the kibbutz was an intricate component of Israeli history and culture, and therefore, he believed that this volunteer work would be very worthwhile.

Before he retired for the evening, he sent another note to Sendi, updating her of his arrival to the Promised Land. He mentioned that he planned to travel to Tel Aviv when he had a break from the toil. Once again, she replied a few days later.

"Thomas,

Mazal tov! This is Hebrew for congratulations for your arrival to this special land. We can meet in café in Tel Aviv when you come here. I wish you good luck with work in kibbutz.

Sendi"

Her reply is on the short side. I am setting the bar low on this high jump (or low jump rather). She did not offer to visit me on the kibbutz; her interest by now seems to be pretty tepid. If her interest were akin to a hot cup of coffee, it's definitely a cup that has been sitting out for a while. Those hotly brewed passions in Paris seem like an eon ago; an arctic blast of air conditioning seems to have intervened in the meantime.

Especially during Japan's winter, Thomas returned home from work without any perspiration. This was never the case here; at the end of every day's work, his clothes were drenched in sweat. *I'm sweating enough here to compete with the amount of water in the Dead Sea.* He had never previously worked a job that required this intensity of physical labor. Although teaching in Japan was extremely draining as well, this work was more physically exhausting. He certainly felt no obligation to do any additional exercise. *In a month, I will be in the leanest physical shape of my life. I will never view a piece of fruit on a plate with the same eyes again! That fruit did not appear in the supermarket as a magic trick. It was produced by grueling toil. Laborers are the most underappreciated human specimens.* True, their work did not require years of schooling and formal education, but regardless, he felt that toil was toil. Toil should be appropriately rewarded, regardless of the level of education required. It required an incredible amount of stamina from the physical body. Teaching was, without a doubt, less grueling in many ways than this work.

He was relieved that this was a mere three-month project and he was not faced with a lifetime of exertion on the plum fields. *My personal washer and dryer wouldn't survive it. My body would need some kind of a warranty policy, or it would be inevitable that I would become redundant from depreciation.* He considered the possibility that if he had grown up in this type of labor-intensive environment, perhaps then he would be tough enough to endure the grueling days without batting an eyelid. But he believed that a lifetime apart from this type of work had caused him to become fundamentally weak in some regards, and therefore, he found the toil to be quite burdensome. *So much of what we can tolerate is due to conditioning. Those early years of life have a monumental influence on our temperament and tolerance later.* "The die is cast" was more than a mere Shakespearean phrase from *Julius Caesar*; Thomas believed that it was fundamental reality, to a large degree. It certainly had greater meaning to him than "Beware the Ides of March"; nothing evil had ever happened to him on March 15, much less a political assassination.

The toil was mitigated to some degree by the camaraderie that he felt with his other fellow volunteers. Fourteen people were volunteering in the date and plum fields, and the community ethos was undeniable. Together, as a team, they were on the front lines of Israel's agricultural economy. The other volunteers spanned the globe on four different continents. Their backgrounds were extremely diverse, and they all originated from widely divergent backgrounds. But here, on these fields, they were all equal. They were equally poor volunteers from a pessimistic point of view and equally adventurous travelers when viewed more positively.

Obviously, people did not volunteer on a kibbutz out of financial motivation. Some individuals did teach English overseas to earn a better living than they otherwise could in their home countries. Some countries in the Gulf paid particularly well after several years of experience, and the East Asian countries of South Korea, Taiwan, and (to a lesser degree) Japan certainly paid livable wages. Kibbutz work was bereft of any meaningful financial reward; it was merely about community and experience. In that respect, it was much more of a "qualitative" endeavor than a quantitative one since the monetary compensation was so minimal. The quantitative numbers were meek, but the qualitative emotions and awareness that resulted from the project were strong.

At the end of his first week working in the fields, he unwound on Saturday evening in the kibbutz bar. The work week in Israel was five and a half days long. They stopped working early on Friday, and then resumed again on Sunday. The bar was not open during the Sabbath, or Shabbat, as it was called in Hebrew. Previously, Thomas was the most familiar with the term "Shabbos" from *The Big Lebowski*. Who could forget Walter screaming, "I don't roll on Shabbos!"

Thomas was learning that Israel was not a completely secular country; aspects of religious Jewish life affected all Israelis, regardless of whether or not they were religious. He also learned that buses did not run during the Sabbath, and nearly all businesses were closed. Although Walter would have been in paradise, Thomas was not pleased to learn these facts. It seemed to be a religious imposition on everyone. In Indiana, he had grown up accepting the separation of church and state as a given. In Israel, it was anything but given.

"Why does the kibbutz bar close during the Sabbath? This is not a religious kibbutz," he noted while drinking at the bar.

Douwe, a thirty-four-year-old Dutch volunteer, had engaged in a lot of reading about Israel prior to his volunteer work. He replied, "Israel began as a deeply secular state when it was founded. However, the religious population has much bigger families. Over time, their numbers have grown a lot and they now have the power in the country. Now Israel is a much more religious state with all of the Sabbath restrictions."

Thomas wondered if the band Black Sabbath had ever written about Israel. Conceivably, they could have written a song about Israeli life. Did Ozzy Osbourne have any knowledge about Israel? He said, "So secular Israelis need to begin having bigger families to gain their power back?"

This thought caused Douwe to chuckle. "Well, you could view it in this light, but it is very expensive to live in Israel. Generally, secular families do not want to bear the costs of so many children. The religious population is much more opposed to birth control, and therefore, their families are much larger. It is often the case throughout the world that more conservative populations have larger families."

"I'm assuming that this demographic shift must also affect politics."

"Oh, certainly. I have deep misgivings about policies here towards the Palestinians. There seemed to be some hope during the nineties that they would make efforts towards peace and the two-state solution. However, now, the chasm between the two sides seems to be unmanageable. The religious Orthodox population is much more opposed to the creation of a Palestinian state and has also supported discriminatory policies towards the Arabs within Israel," Douwe said.

"So out of curiosity, Douwe, why are you doing this volunteer work? I find your viewpoints to be very interesting, but I have not heard these views in the country in my brief time here."

"I am impressed with Israeli agriculture and I am intrigued by the concept of a kibbutz. I wanted to see kibbutz life firsthand. In general, I like many Israelis. I do not want you to take away the impression that I am an Israel-hater. I just have reservations about the current political situation and without a doubt, I prefer the more liberal Israelis. The kibbutz itself is a somewhat liberal concept, and it is a legacy of Israel's early days."

"I have heard people make similar comments to me about the United States. They say that they like many Americans on a personal level, but they do not like the government. It is entirely feasible to distinguish the nation from the state. People who administer the government often produce a very different impression than the 'normal' citizenry. American political policy is extremely pro-Israel, so it is refreshing to hear a European viewpoint here that questions the occupation."

"Absolutely. I am deeply disgusted by American coddling of Israel. The human rights abuses must end, and there needs to be a path towards a respectful co-existence between the two states. If I had openly blogged about my opposition to the occupation, I do not know if I would have been admitted to the country. However, since my opposition is only oral in this bar tonight, I am able to volunteer here. The current Israeli government attempts to keep out foreigners who are strongly and openly opposed to their policies."

"You're not worried that they will deport you from the country?"

"Not for merely speaking about the conflict. There isn't a Russian-style KGB that videotapes all ordinary conversations. However, as I said, if I had been a strong political activist against Israel and had, for example, participated on some of the flotillas that attempted to bring goods to the Palestinian territories, then I am very confident that my volunteer visa would not have been approved."

Camila, a volunteer from Costa Rica, was also in the bar within earshot of their conversation. Douwe knew her from working together on common tasks.

"What do you think about the current conflict, Camila?" he asked.

She turned towards them. "I lived in Israel for five years as a child. My father was diplomat in the Costa Rican embassy and I attend international school. Douwe, the conflict is very complicated. Can you really say it is just human rights abuse on Israeli side?

"Perhaps not. There is hatred on the Palestinian side also, but I believe that there is strong evidence that there have been human rights abuses on the Israeli side."

"I feel a lot of hate from both sides. Hate seems to cause more hate in a cycle. I do not think Israel can just end occupation tomorrow. How do they know they will not get attack and invasion?"

"Camila, I agree that the conflict is complex. I do not want to say only Israel has done wrong. But the Israeli government is not helping with the peace process. How can there be a solution when the government keeps building settlements and seizing more land?"

"I agree with you about settlement expansion. But I understand why they are afraid of Hamas. Hamas want to put them in the sea, they have said."

At this point, Thomas chimed in, "It is difficult to understand the conflict well when I am not from here. I feel very much as an outsider looking in at this extremely multidimensional conflict. Especially being from the United States, which is such a young country, it is difficult to fully grasp the attachments that the Jews and Muslims have here to these ancient sites. Control over these sites and this land that they consider to be holy seems to be driving this interminable conflict."

"I am not familiar with interminable word. What does it mean?" Camila asked.

"Something without an end."

"Ah yes, that describes very well this conflict. I want to be optimistic that in three hundred years, this conflict will be over, but I find it challenging to be optimistic on this conflict," she said.

Thomas replied, "I do not wish to be overly judgmental about the Israeli side. They are surrounded by hostile countries. It is quite a contrast to the geography of the United States, where we feel quite secure. No doubt, this kind of geography here could make any reasonable person a bit paranoid. But I do agree that the current policies are not particularly conducive towards peace. I am not as deeply familiar with the situation as Douwe. I had never heard about 'human rights abuses' associated with Israel until he mentioned it tonight. Douwe, what is an example of human rights abuses on the Israeli side?"

Douwe immediately responded, "After an attack or suicide bombing, they have a common practice of destroying the home of the attacker. They punish the entire family for the actions of one person. This, I believe, is a deep human rights abuse."

"I see. Yes, I have ethical objections to that type of practice as well. I do not believe that it is rational to believe that parents can control all actions of their children," Thomas noted.

"It strongly harms their image internationally every time that this is done. In Europe, I have felt a strong tide turning against Israel in the last fifteen years, and these kinds of practices must end for this trend to change."

Thomas did not feel that there was significant disagreement among the three of them. He thought that they were all pragmatic thinkers and not extremists. However, the extremists were driving the conflict. Percentage wise, a small number of people were doing an immense amount of damage. *It is helpful to have a chance to observe the conflict on the ground rather than merely have it fed through the American media.* In the coming weeks when he would be traveling to Jerusalem and Tel Aviv, he hoped to learn additional angles and viewpoints with regard to the conflict.

After another month of grueling labor on the kibbutz, he had earned some vacation time. It was now time to explore the large cities of Israel. The kibbutz was a marvelous mix of backgrounds and nationalities, but geographically, it was quite isolated. He believed there was a limit to how much knowledge that he could obtain about the country from date and plum fields. He needed to see the urban metropolises.

Should he sojourn to Tel Aviv or Jerusalem first? He contacted his former teaching companion Saul, who strongly recommended that he first go to Tel Aviv. Saul said that from a tourism point of view, Jerusalem was the crowning achievement of a visit to Israel, and therefore, he should "save the best for last". Thomas disagreed with this line of reasoning; he had seen Kyoto before Tokyo in Japan, and he did not believe that it adversely affected his experience. Yes, Tokyo had less for tourists than Kyoto. It lacked the deep history and endless temples, but it still had intrinsic value. It was still a bustling city with interesting neighborhoods and a distinct vibe compared to Kyoto. Tokyo was Tokyo and Kyoto was Kyoto. They were both stimulating journeys and he believed that the sequence in which they were seen was merely an afterthought rather than something that was of fundamental importance.

Leaving all that aside, Thomas was more curious about Tel Aviv and so for that reason was inclined to follow Saul's suggestion. Although Jerusalem was undoubtedly the more historical place, he had been told by multiple people that Tel Aviv was the party capital of Israel and brimming with nightlife. At the moment, this whetted his curiosity more than Jerusalem's deep history. Historical sites were not the only means of casual travel; often, people-watching was just as fascinating. Tel Aviv was the newer, more modern city. In his currently ahistorical mood, he desired modernity more. It was undeniably true that Sendi was also in Tel Aviv, but his expectations about meeting her were quite low. Furthermore, after the Spartan, "back to nature" type surroundings of a kibbutz, he coveted its polar opposite. Jerusalem's historicity would have to be shelved on layaway for now. Modern bustle was the mood of the moment.

He followed up again with Sendi about having coffee in Tel Aviv. She replied,

"Thomas,

I will be happy to drink a coffee with you. I have been dating a man here for couple months, so I do not want you to have wrong impression. But if you want to meet again, we can have coffee. How is life in kibbutz?

Sendi"

He slightly crumbled inside. A few crumbs had fallen off the cake rather than the entire cake falling to the floor. Her response was certainly a depressant rather than a stimulant, but indeed, her last message had contained an undertone of reduced interest. This email was hardly a wildcard. He decided that meeting Sendi now would just reawaken the feelings that he'd had, and therefore, would be more harmful than advantageous. It was time to close the book on this impractical fling, and focus his energies on absorbing Israel generally. He had been wise to have measured expectations about Sendi from the beginning, and his decision to come to Israel was based on several considerations, not merely her. He did not have a trace of regret that he had decided to spend a few months in Israel. It was a refreshing change from Japan, and a fascinating culture to boot. Some days, he considered the hummus alone to be worth the price of admission.

As he arrived in Tel Aviv at the bus station, he began meandering around the city center. When he first saw the women walking the streets, he did a double take. He had seen a few gorgeous women on the plane, but this trend was now multiplied tenfold. It was no wonder that Sendi had previously remarked that she was merely "normal" here. *Is every woman here a model?* Both the male and female population was extremely fit; overweight people were extremely rare. The Mediterranean climate here must be very fortunate for the skin. Many of the women on the plane journey had stunning olive skin, and this metaphorical road now had become a ten-lane highway in bustling Tel Aviv. He wasn't attracted to light, pale skin and he also was not attracted to skin that was too dark. This olive skin was the perfect balance. *I will yearn for these views when I have returned to Indiana's gray landscape. Sun, or its lack thereof, does have a large influence on the attractiveness of the population,* he now realized. *I wish that I had that kind of skin; who wouldn't desire beautiful skin?*

As his people-watching session continued over the next couple of hours, Thomas heard people speaking both Hebrew and Arabic. By now, he had heard enough of both languages to be able to differentiate them. The two languages were highly "throat-oriented", but Arabic seemed to have harder sounds. He did not hear a large amount of Arabic in this section of Tel Aviv, but it had a small presence. He knew that the Jaffa part of the Tel Aviv area had a much larger Arab population.

However, without hearing them speak, he could not distinguish many of the Arabs from the tanner looking Jews in the city. He later learned that the Jews in Israel were primarily divided into two groups: Ashkenazi and Sephardic. The Ashkenazi Jews were from Central and Eastern Europe, had lighter skin, and on average, were wealthier and better educated in Israel than the Sephardim. Saul, his coworker in Japan, was an Ashkenazi Jew, as was the case for most American Jews. The Sephardic Jews, on the other hand, were originally from Spain, Portugal, and the Middle East. They tended to have more of the "blue collar" jobs and they had fewer positions of power in business and the government. They had much darker skin, and in many cases, Thomas could not distinguish them from Arabs.

Furthermore, unlike the walled-in kibbutz, security personnel were a dime a dozen in the city. He was searched for weapons before entering both a supermarket and a mall. The threat of terrorism was clearly an everyday feature of life here; it wasn't merely an aspect of flying, as it was in the United States. Undergoing searches merely upon entering a supermarket would be a profound mental adjustment, he believed. It certainly altered the mood of daily life. Thomas had participated in some discussions on the kibbutz with the Israeli personnel about their fears of terrorism, and they had said that they had become accustomed to dealing with it. Israelis are born into a permanent state of cold war, they said. From a young age, the Israelis become very familiar with being alert for possible terrorism and the threat of attacks.

The Cold War in the United States had ended in the late twentieth century, but there was no such end in this land. The Israelis on the kibbutz had said that few of them believed that the situation would significantly change in their lifetimes; the tensions between them and the surrounding Arab populations had festered for centuries. *In the United States, we are too young to have these deep hatreds. In some respects, being such a young country is quite advantageous.* In this region, erasing this hatred and mistrust appeared to be quite daunting. Was it possible to teach people here to forget about the past in order to create a harmonious future? Disregarding the past seemed strongly to conflict with the cultural codes here. History here was much more than skin deep; it penetrated hard to the bone. One of the Israelis on the kibbutz had said that events in 1929 were akin to yesterday here; eighty years was perceived in terms of days, much less decades.

Thomas spent the night in a youth hostel; hotel prices in Tel Aviv were stratospherically expensive. Many of them had a daily cost that exceeded his entire three-month stipend at the kibbutz. Once again, he slept in a room with multiple bunk beds. One Israeli man in the room, Avi, had been staying at the hostel for a couple of weeks.

"Do you really like this hostel if you have been here for two weeks?" Thomas asked.

Avi laughed. "I cannot pay hotel room in Tel Aviv. Tel Aviv is very expensive city, even more than normal cost of Israel. Where you come from?"

"Indiana, in the United States."

"Indiana...this is in the middle of America?"

"Indeed. We even call that region 'Middle America', meaning that it has a large percentage of average, everyday kind of people."

Avi gazed at him with sudden focus, and made stronger eye contact. "I see. Yes, many Israelis travel to United States. You have very rich country. Why are you in Israel? Are you Jewish?"

"No, a Jewish colleague of mine suggested that I come here after teaching in Japan. He said that the direct nature of the Israelis would be a nice change and interesting contrast to Japan."

"Sorry...repeat part of Israelis."

"My friend said that Israelis are direct. This would be a nice change from Japan."

Avi gave a large grin. "I see. Yes, you always know what is in our mind. We do not try to hide things from people. Do they do this in Japan?"

"I would say yes. The Japanese language even has different words for the inner mind and outer mind."

"That is very interesting. In Israel, they are the same. But some Israelis can be very pushy. I have talked to tourists who did not like."

Unruffled, Thomas replied, "Well, I definitely feel more comfortable here than I did in Japan. I would much rather have some pushy people instead of constantly feeling as though I am in a difficult maze of understanding."

"Did you meet the American Jews at home?"

"No, there are not many in Indiana."

"I have met many who come to Israel. Yes, they seem very American compared to us. They are not as direct like us. I have met a few who love to criticize our politics. It is very easy to criticize when you are hundreds of miles away in mighty America. Here, we are on the front lines of a difficult conflict."

If Douwe's views were the head of the coin, now I am hearing the tail. "So no criticism should be tolerated?"

"Well, if you live here and try to understand, then I will listen more to your criticism. If you live in a fancy apartment in New York City or Chicago and want to criticize us, then you are crossing a line."

It's best now to turn down the temperature on this oven. "I'm really here to learn about the culture, not get involved in a big debate about the Israeli–Palestinian conflict. I realize that it is very complicated," Thomas replied.

Avi smiled. "There is lots of culture in Israel. You will get much during your time here."

"What makes you stay in this youth hostel for two weeks?"

"I am searching for work in Tel Aviv. I come from a smaller town about two hours from here. The Tel Aviv area has much opportunity, but it is very expensive. Most of us in Israel struggle with economics. We have a very expensive country. America is fortunate to have its level of wealth."

Thomas nodded a couple of times. "Yes, we are lucky in many ways in America. I do appreciate this aspect more after living in some other places. What kind of work do you do?"

"I am engineer. I am searching for tech company work here. Tel Aviv has many tech company. We are always starting new companies as well. Israel has very big startup culture. We are second after Silicon Valley as hub for startups. Did you know that?"

"I knew that a little bit, but I am not intimately familiar with why this is the case."

"We are very creative, always coming up with new idea. Then we want to test the new idea. Entrepreneurial spirit is very strong in Israel."

"Yes, it does seem to be the case that there is a very skilled workforce here. I have also met many humorous people here," Thomas noted with a slight smirk.

"We are always making the jokes. Otherwise, the life is too boring," he replied.

As Thomas continued to explore the streets of Tel Aviv the next day, he noticed a large number of restaurants with food from the former Soviet Union. He observed restaurants with Ukrainian dumplings on the menu, Russian borscht soup, and Georgian food (this did not include sweet iced tea or fried chicken). His internet research revealed that there were over one million people in Israel from the former Soviet Union, especially Russia. Israel had Russian newspapers and Russian radio stations as well.

A Russian population of one million in the United States would not be particularly significant, percentage wise. However, in the tiny land of Israel, this was a huge percentage. In addition to diversifying a Middle Eastern-dominated food scene, Thomas imagined that it strongly broadened the wider cultural landscape as well. *There truly are Jews here from the world over.* The Jewish diaspora, which had wide tentacles throughout the globe, had congregated from all of its alleys and boulevards onto this Lilliputian-sized strip of land.

Although the Russian restaurants looked appealing, they were also quite pricey. A more economical option was eating at a simple chicken shawarma type restaurant; these places had the cheapest food in Israel, though the food remained fresh and tasty. Thomas picked up a "pita wrap" here, and the cashier placed his change on the counter. Thomas was expecting to be given his change, and therefore indicated that he was still waiting for it. The man grunted loudly and abruptly pointed over at the coins on the counter. Thomas grabbed the coins and walked away. *Very Israeli customer service. No country is perfect. I have to accept the darkness and light in every country.* The Israelis were very warm and sincere, but the abrupt service required a mental adjustment. *This is the culture here; I cannot take this personally. Overall, I still gravitate towards a fondness for this society compared to Japan.*

No visit to Tel Aviv was complete without visiting the beach. Saul had described Tel Aviv as a mixture of Miami and New York City, and Thomas now understood why Saul had chosen these cities. The New York City comparison was obvious, due to its large Jewish presence, its largely secular, freewheeling nature, and the emphasis on commerce and business. On the other hand, New York City was lacking a beach presence; here Miami filled in that gap (with bounteous waves).

The beach seemed to set the mood of the city in numerous ways. The people in Tel Aviv were extremely fit, and had great bodies to show off at the beach. Olive skin, toned muscles for the men, and many model-like bodies for the women. This city was a visual feast in numerous different respects. Most of these women were not pretty; they were gorgeous. He had never seen this kind of beauty before on this scale. *These people are very intelligent and extremely attractive. If they were in a safer part of the world, this would be Heaven.*

When he returned to the hostel for the night, he dove into bed. However, he was still up a few hours later. This was not because the hostel itself was particularly boisterous. No, he was a "victim" of the well-attended Tel Aviv club scene. Hordes of young people in the city were partying until late into the night. Even at 3:00 a.m., he heard large groups coming out of the clubs, shouting loudly. Regularly, he heard the clatter of beer bottles landing in garbage cans. Clearly, Tel Aviv was the epicenter of nightlife in the country. Other Israelis had commented to him that this was the case, and now he unequivocally believed it. Traditional Judaism was not the religion here; hedonism was.

When he was growing up in Indiana, Thomas had assumed that Judaism was predominantly a religion, but surely these Tel Aviv citizens also qualified as "Jewish"? Or were they merely Jew-"ish"? No, that wasn't right. Thomas still believed that Tel Aviv was a fundamentally Jewish city. Judaism went beyond merely religious teachings; it was a nation and culture as well. He predicted that sleeping in Jerusalem would be much easier; that city had a fundamentally different ethos and had never been labeled as a party city.

The bus journey to Jerusalem was quite brief; he was, after all, in a country that was the size of New Jersey. Fundamentally, a spread-out landscape was not a feature of Israeli life. Taking a step back, it was remarkable how much history was present here in such a tiny strip of land. Indiana, on the whole, was primarily ahistorical. It was a younger state and had few extremely significant events in American history. Israel was its polar opposite. Historical landmarks here were omnipresent; even a young drunk youth from Tel Aviv who was stumbling around surely would land on history in most of the country. Malcolm X, when he was discussing black history, had famously said something similar to, "We didn't land on Plymouth Rock; Plymouth Rock landed on us." Likewise, in Israel, you did not land on history; history landed on you.

On the bus, he was sitting next to a man with a large, very thick beard, and earlocks. He was wearing a black top hat, a white shirt, and a long black coat. *Is this Rincewind the wizard from*

Terry Pratchett's Discworld? Then he remembered the reading that he had done a couple of weeks ago on the kibbutz. The book mentioned this sub-population of Israel: the Hasidic Jews. Saul had also mentioned them when he had "briefed" Thomas about his upcoming Israeli experience. The Hasidim were also called the Ultra-Orthodox and were the equivalent of the Amish in a Jewish context. They were the strictest, most conservative Jews, and they took religious teachings the most literally. Like the Amish, they had distinctive dress and they sequestered them-selves into separate communities. They attended educational institutions called yeshivas; yeshivas omitted many subjects from the curriculum, such as Science, Math, English, etc. Instead, there was a much stronger focus on studying the Torah (the first five books of the Bible) and the Talmud, which was an extremely long Jewish legal text.

If Israel's historicity was the polar opposite of Indiana, the Hasidic Jews were the polar opposites of the hard-partying youths of Tel Aviv. Women were required to dress extremely conservatively; even if the woman were as gorgeous as the hordes of women in Tel Aviv, it would be much less obvious. The aura of "fashion models" that he felt in the streets of Tel Aviv was an entire universe away in the Hasidic community. Men and women also prayed separately in Hasidic and Orthodox synagogues. This practice was similar to Islam, another very conservative religion.

The Hasidic man's dress seemed quite medieval to Thomas; he felt as though he were sitting next to a time traveler from the 1300's. He was highly tempted to ask the man if he knew anyone who had suffered from the bubonic plague, but he figured that his comment would not be appreciated. Asking him if he were a wizard would be even worse, assuming that the man spoke English. English did not seem to be a highly prominent aspect of

Israeli life; the percentage of English speakers here seemed to be roughly equivalent to Japan. Although on the whole, Japan and Israel seemed to occupy different galaxies, they did both seem to be highly insular societies that preferred to avoid English as much as possible.

Thomas had heard about countries that were very English-oriented, such as Malaysia or Sweden. However, on his journey so far, he had yet to spend time in a country that "liked" speaking English as a foreign language. (Obviously his brief time in England was in a different category.) Instead, in France, Japan, and Israel, English seemed to be more of an annoyance to the general population. He was sympathetic to these feelings; it was extremely difficult to learn another language, especially if the language was highly different from the native tongue. This especially applied to the inhabitants of Japan and Israel; when they learned English, they had to learn a new alphabet in addition to everything else. In Hebrew, the written text moved from right to left. In Japanese, the verb came at the end of the sentence. In some cases, Japanese sentence structure was closer to Yoda's speaking style. For example, Yoda said, "Truly wonderful, the mind of a child is."

Very few people would embrace English with zealous enthusiasm under these circumstances. In this respect, it was quite fortuitous that he had been born in the United States. Learning another language was *optional*, not mandatory. Everywhere that he went, he could find people who spoke English. This was not the case with any other language, though languages such as French and Spanish did have wide global footprints. It was highly educational to learn another language, but undeniably, it was also a burden. Americans, with their current global power, were the entitled ones in this context. "Speak our language, world", the United States was essentially saying and now, after several decades of global hegemony, this had become a *fait accompli*.

As he exited the bus and began walking through the city, he was definitely no longer in Tel Aviv. Buff, athletic-looking guys had been replaced by Orthodox Jews in skullcaps. The beach had been replaced by numerous yeshivas. Tel Aviv was a young city, less than two hundred years old; Jerusalem was more akin to an ancient wonder of the world. The climate was also a stark contrast compared to Tel Aviv. Tel Aviv had spring-like weather nearly year round, and limitless sun to accompany the beaches. Jerusalem was much colder, windier, and cloudier. If a dark apocalypse were ever to come thundering down from the heavens in this uber-Semitic New Jersey, it would be in Jerusalem, not Tel Aviv.

On one level, he believed that the climate enhanced the antiqueness of the city. Traditional Judaism was serious business. A city with a plethora of sun-filled beaches didn't fit the bill as appropriately as this climate. The demands of traditional religion were not analogous to taking it easy on a beach; they were much more equivalent to walking through Jerusalem's darker, windy streets. Practicing traditional religion involved giving up many temptations. For example, it was required to fast on Yom Kippur. Likewise, it was necessary to fight cold winds and more frequent inclement weather in Jerusalem. Any religion that did seem equivalent to beach chilling should be regarded with the utmost suspicion, he believed. As an atheist, he already regarded all religions with deep skepticism, but the skepticism was even more pronounced towards a beach bum kind of faith. If there were an afterlife, the admission ticket should require true diligence and grit. Any faith promising an undemanding beach ride surely was a scam.

Thomas spent the night in another youth hostel near the city center. Here, the streets were mostly deserted by 9:30 p.m. He perceived a library-like silence in the streets outside. Sleeping tonight would involve few, if any, interruptions. The hedonist lifestyle of Tel Aviv seemed to be much more than an hour away; it was in a completely different space-time continuum.

The next day, Thomas visited the most famous place in Jerusalem: the Western Wall. His travel book mentioned that this site was often called the "Wailing Wall", but this term was mostly used by Christians during the times of Christian control of the city. When the Romans controlled the city, the Jews were prohibited from entering Jerusalem except for attending Tisha be-Av, which was the day of national mourning for the temples. Therefore, Jewish activity at the Wall consisted primarily of weeping. The term was also used during British rule of the city. Because of this historical context, the term "Wailing Wall" was now considered to be disrespectful.

This was enough persuasion for Thomas to avoid this term. Just as there was a common American expression that said: "Don't mess with Texas", he had been in this country long enough to know that it was similarly wise to refrain from messing with Israel. The tight security at the airport had clearly established that precedent; you messed with them at your peril. Most likely, many people would not realize the connotation of the term "Wailing Wall", and therefore, it was still used sometimes. He doubted it would result in anyone being expelled from the country, but the serious milieu of Jerusalem suggested caution rather than heedlessness. People had died for thousands of years battling over this tiny speck of earth; this was not just any other locale.

Within that frame of reference, this visit represented still another milestone in his travel history. France and Japan had "old" places, but they were significantly younger than Jerusalem. This was the first place that he had visited that truly went back to the years "before Christ". There were few experiences that rivaled visiting Jerusalem; it was a noteworthy city for three major religions. This was simply a vastly different place than most tourist destinations. He also realized that this was his final tourist stopover before he returned to the United States; his tourist visa would be expiring soon, and he desired to take a break before embarking on any further travel. It was challenging to imagine a more meaningful place to conclude his long travel odyssey, which had begun in Bordeaux, France. He did not view it as "saving the best for last"; he believed that this was comparing apples and oranges. France, Japan, and Israel each had their unique charms. Therefore, it was foolish to argue that Jerusalem was necessarily the "best". But undoubtedly, it was both a uniquely historical and uniquely religious city.

As a secular person, it was a lofty endeavor to feel a tangible impact from Jerusalem's religiosity. Thomas primarily viewed the city through a historical lens rather than a religious one. It was a necessity that any true history student would appreciate religion's impact on humanity, even if he did not believe in its tenets. Yes, for Thomas, Jerusalem was archaeology on steroids. Within the context of human longevity, Jerusalem was the Japanese woman who was 118 years old. It had outlasted nearly all of its competitors. It was unfortunate that the city was such a divisive flashpoint between warring faiths, but religion was contentious by its very nature. Thomas believed that belief systems that made grandiose claims about the supernatural and human salvation would inevitably lead to conflict.

The Western Wall was extremely crowded; even though it was

a Wednesday, the site was packed with people. A yarmulke or head covering was required to enter the grounds. Thomas had left his baseball cap at the youth hostel; it was a less obvious need in cloudy Jerusalem compared to Tel Aviv, where the sun was extremely powerful. Therefore, he borrowed one of the yarmulkes. He felt a tiny bit Jewish today from wearing the skullcap. Saul had "anointed" him as an honorary Jew back in Japan based on his sense of humor. Today, he shared a superficial likeness with the Jews around him who were praying at the Wall.

The Wall had separate sections for men and women, following the teachings of traditional Judaism. There was also a common practice of leaving notes in the cracks of the Wall. Thomas was quite intrigued by this practice; he learned on his phone that over a million notes were left each year by tourists and diplomats. Twice a year, the notes were collected and buried in the Mount of Olives, which was nearby. Clearly, he would not be leaving a note of a religious nature, but he desired to leave behind some kind of brief missive. He wrote a note that simply expressed a hunger for peace in the area. Most likely, thousands had previously left similar notes in these cracks; there would be no prizes for originality. But unfortunately, especially in Jerusalem, he felt hate in the air: hatred between Jews and Arabs. Arabs lived in one part of the city, and the tension was unmistakable. Since this apprehension was at the forefront of his mind, this would be his note for the occasion.

The tension created an extremely yin and yang feeling. He was both in awe of the archaeology and historical tradition, and extremely repelled by the lack of harmony among the inhabitants of the city. Peace at this point in time seemed as distant as Jupiter. In a particularly cynical moment, he believed that humans would inhabit Jupiter before there would be peace in either Jerusalem, or Israel as a whole.

He was light years from being an expert on the conflict, but it seemed to be a particularly toxic brew of two parties who both fervently believed that God unconditionally supported their point of view. When the conviction level of a belief reached that degree of certainty, it created a formidable obstacle towards any meaningful dialogue or resolution. Perhaps it was a necessary condition to be a theist in order to have any faith in a peaceful solution to this conflict; at this point, it seemed to be the case that only a divine miracle would provide peace. As an atheist, it was beyond the bounds of possibility to believe in miracles. But how could there be peaceful harmony here without one party being completely annihilated? Absent a horrifying genocidal extermination, peace seemed to be as bleak of a possibility as a lake swim during an Indiana winter.

Before he had traveled to Israel, he sincerely believed in at least the possibility of peace. But now, after experiencing the actual atmosphere of Jerusalem and rubbing shoulders with the inhabitants, all of those possibilities had vanished in his mind. The throngs of Orthodox Jews walking through the streets inspired few assurances of progress. On this issue, he had been transformed from a discouraged cynic to an utterly despondent one. He yearned for a few millimeters of hope for a way out of this quagmire, but no such millimeters were to be found.

He had never felt this demoralized about a political issue before. The United States, France, and Japan did not have this level of tension. He wondered if this was a uniquely Middle Eastern phenomenon; in order to test this claim, numerous more world voyages would be required. For now, it would remain as a somewhat plausible hypothesis.

Adherence to deep historical traditions contained possibilities for both wisdom and fanatical acrimony. He hoped that there was a conceivable path out of this abyss. At best, during his lifetime, could the conflict be transformed from a horror novel to a science fiction novel? Science fiction novels at least represented human possibility if not human actuality. If Israeli–Palestinian peace had a component of human possibility at some point in his lifetime, then that would be monumental progress.

In addition to delving into the wonders of the Western Wall, Thomas planned to explore the remainder of the Old City before leaving Jerusalem. Jerusalem's Old City was divided into four quarters: Jewish, Christian, Muslim, and Armenian. Why was there an Armenian Quarter? This definitely seemed to be the part of the Sesame Street skit where one part does not belong with the others. Thomas researched the issue and found that the Armenian Quarter was the smallest one. *Logically speaking, was it a true "quarter" if it were smaller than the other three?* He learned that the Armenians were Christians, but they, along with their Patriarchate, remained independent. Jordan controlled all four quarters of the Old City after 1948, and imposed regulations on private Christian schools that required equal study time for both the Bible and the Koran. After the 1967 war, Jordan relinquished control, and five hundred Armenians remained in the quarter, along with three thousand Armenians in greater Jerusalem.

Even though Jerusalem was controlled by the Jews and the neighboring population was predominantly Muslim, Christianity had two of the four quarters. This further demonstrated how profoundly Jerusalem represented all three monotheistic faiths. There were few Christians in the area as a percentage of the whole, but regardless, they had two quarters in this holy city. Why had so many monotheistic religions developed here? Was it because the area had a "head start" in terms of human population compared to many other areas? Or were they merely "lucky" (or unlucky, depending on your viewpoint) that these teachings gained a following here, and then spread like wildfire to the other corners of the earth? The only other geographical locale that could claim any parity in terms of religious influence was India; it had "developed" Hinduism and Buddhism, which were also practiced by an enormous proportion of the world's population.

Why did these two places have such an outsized influence on the world's religious teachings? Did prophets gain a larger following in warmer, more temperate climates? Was high population density also a necessity? At that moment, Thomas was curious if any academic scholars had attempted to answer these questions. He believed that, surely, he was not the first person to ask this question; it hardly struck him as a deeply original thought.

Returning back to his local surroundings, he learned that the Christian Quarter had the Church of the Holy Sepulchre; many people believed that this was Christianity's holiest place. This place was also referred to as the Church of the Resurrection or Church of the Anastasis by Orthodox Christians. Here, Jesus was crucified, and it also contained his "empty tomb", in which he was buried and resurrected. Several Christian denominations shared control over the site: Greek Orthodox, Armenian Orthodox, Roman Catholic, and a few other less-known denominations controlled a smaller portion. He also learned that Protestants had a very minimal presence here; they were more inclined to believe that the Garden Tomb, which was in another part of Jerusalem, was the true place of Christ's crucifixion.

The Muslim Quarter was the largest in both area and population. Thomas saw many shopping markets in this area. They sold a huge variety of products: jewelry, electronics, textiles, produce, meat, and spices. He also learned, through his research, that there were many Israeli settlements in this part. This was little surprise, now that he had built up some knowledge about the conflict.

The Jewish Quarter had a quite deep history that dated back to the eighth century before Christ. The Jews were forced to leave the area during the 1948 war, and then returned after Israel resumed control in 1967. During this time, Israel ordered that the then-Moroccan Quarter be demolished in order to allow access to the Western Wall. The Temple Mount, which was important to all three faiths, was also here. The famous Al-Aqsa Mosque was located in this complex. Furthermore, many synagogues and yeshivas were now located in this quarter.

Thomas spent nearly a day wandering through these four quarters. Although the Old City was only .35 square miles in area, it was "nutrient rich". He realized that this day was a notable "compass point" in his travels. Most likely, he would never again be in a confined area that was so monumental to all three monotheistic faiths. He was a true eyewitness to Biblical and Koranic history here. For a moment, he reminisced back to that early college conversation with Sean in his dormitory, in which Sean extolled the virtues of golf and blasted the uselessness of history. He wished that Sean could be here in these quarters for just a few minutes. If Sean still believed that history was meaningless, then he would completely abandon hope on his potential for historical appreciation. But Thomas was skeptical that Sean would cling to the same ideas if he were able to breathe these spiritual fumes. Sean's viewpoint was a product of his experiences, and his experiences had unquestionably lacked anything like this.

I am extremely fortunate to be in these surroundings at this juncture. The small-town Indiana boy has perished from the earth; I am now a global citizen flanked by Christianity, Judaism, and Islam, all of which are a stone's throw away from me. I can never return to being a person with limited life experiences; the past couple of years have forever altered my perceptions, beliefs, and outlook. The top of my Pandora's travel box is not even in the local sky anymore; it has migrated to a different star that is light years away. If Sean and I had difficulty understanding each other back then in the dormitory, imagine how wide the gulf would be now? At that time, I at least viewed myself as an American. Now I have relinquished that label in favor of global citizen. If I were a traveler from another country when I spoke to Sean before, now I would be a visitor from a different planet or solar system. A foreigner has been morphed into an extraterrestrial. If I experience thirty more countries, what will my identity become then? A turbo-extraterrestrial?

Thomas returned to the kibbutz with two weeks remaining on his tourist visa. He completed two more weeks of arduous labor, but his mind was firmly focused on the indefinite future. Previously, he had known that he would be traveling to France, Japan, and Israel, respectively as next steps. Other than returning home, he was undecided where he was headed. Thomas strongly wondered how he would perceive the external stimuli once he returned home. He had been overseas for a significant period of time; would he still recognize Indiana? Undoubtedly yes, but it did not seem feasible to believe that his perceptions would be unchanged. He also believed that it was fruitless to over-speculate about this topic until he returned to Indiana soil.

He mentioned to several of his kibbutz colleagues that they were welcome to stay with him if they ever visited the United States, freely acknowledging that the probability of any of them visiting Indiana was similar to the chance of Israeli–Palestinian peace. He also mentioned that there was a possibility that he would relocate to a more frequently visited destination in the U.S. He lacked strong intentions to settle in Indiana.

His domestic travel in the United States had been utterly nonexistent; now with his new multi-continent perspective, it seemed to be a wise idea to explore some of the more cosmopolitan areas of the United States and then assimilate these experiences into his updated psychological model. How much overlap would he find between San Francisco and Paris? Would New York City now feel highly comparable to London? Would he find the history in Boston impressive, or would it feel like child's play compared to Israel's history? All of these questions were, as yet, unresolved.

7

Chapter Seven

February 2017

The most economical flight back to Indianapolis was with United Airlines; as much as he would have preferred another mouth-watering Israeli meal on El Al, his pocketbook was not in accord with this choice. Since his future plans were so tentative, it seemed especially unwise at this point in time to spend money unnecessarily. He had exhausted nearly all of his savings from Japan during his time in Israel. His expenses on the kibbutz were covered for the most part, but the travel to Tel Aviv and Jerusalem had been costly. Israel was an extremely expensive country.

Instead, he had to settle for more pedestrian American fare on the United flight. It was back to ordinary sandwiches, meat, and potatoes. The flight attendants certainly came across as uber-polite compared to the ones on El Al. Yes, he was returning to the land of please and thank you. The lack of traditional courtesy in Israel had failed to ruffle his feathers; he had been much more annoyed by the extreme politeness in Japan. Overall, he liked the Israelis. He appreciated their sincerity and found them to be extremely warm people, generally speaking. Israel suited his temperament infinitely better than Japan.

He had also developed a more comfortable feeling in Israel compared to France, though the gulf was much narrower compared to Japan. There were many similarities between Israel and France: strong food cultures, a lot of misogynistic attitudes towards women, strong government welfare programs, heavy emphasis on education and health care, psychotic drivers, and a lot of abrupt, aggressive, in-your-face people. Of course, there were innumerable differences as well. Israel was a fundamentally Jewish society and was much more technologically cutting edge than France. France had a more harmonious relationship with other countries on the world stage and was wealthier and less crowded. Culinary wise, France was much more oriented towards wine and dairy products such as cheese and butter. He had enjoyed his time in France, but his gut instinct gravitated more towards the Israelis as people. Their hospitality was much more pronounced, and he had felt more welcome as a "guest".

As the plane descended into Indianapolis airport, Thomas had a strange feeling in his stomach. Here he was, landing in another country. But this was not merely any other country on the map; this was his native land. Here, he could enter the citizens' line and be faced with few questions about financial resources or purpose of stay. Come to think of it, what was he actually going to be doing here now? But from the legalistic viewpoint of Immigration, his purpose of stay was clear: he was returning home.

As he descended the plane and walked through the airport, reverse culture shock immediately penetrated his consciousness. Nearly everyone was speaking English! He could understand easily the surrounding conversations; they were not veiled in a maze of throat-intensive Hebrew, rhythmical Japanese, or romantic French. Nor were they speaking English in unfamiliar Australian, Irish, or English accents. It was, once again, significantly more difficult to tune out others around him. Returning home would require headphones.

His interview at Immigration merely lasted a couple of minutes. The agent asked him why he had gone to France, Japan, and Israel. He seemed to be satisfied with his answers, and in classic American fashion, he wished him a nice day.

Security personnel at this airport were principally at their machines, not roaming around searching for suspicious people. Although security had notably increased in the United States after the September 11, 2001 terrorist attacks, it was a more tranquil feeling in the airport when matched against Israel. Compared to Israeli airports, a hospital operating room felt relaxed.

Therefore, there were fewer "checkpoints" here. Yes, checkpoints were as common as water in Israel, both in the airport and throughout the Palestinian territories. Thomas could not think of another image that better represented a nation under siege than Israel's myriad checkpoints; the feeling of being threatened was ubiquitous. Attempting to run away from this feeling was as productive as striving to avoid the molecules in the air; the siege fear was an organic property of Israel's emotional chemistry. As Doc Brown might have said in *Back to the Future*, eliminating this property might unravel the very fabric of the space-time continuum itself. Great Scott!

After he exited Immigration and Customs, he met his parents, who were ready to drive him back to his hometown of Albany, Indiana. His mother was shaking with excitement when she saw him after his extended absence. She ran up and grabbed his arm. Neither of his parents had been enthusiastic about his decision to leave the country. They exchanged few words during the ride home; it did not feel significantly different than riding in a taxi, with a driver who spoke limited English. His parents had virtually no travel experience of any kind, and therefore, they could not relate to his experiences. They primarily discussed what his future plans would be now that he had returned to Indiana.

During the next couple of weeks, reverse culture shock faded and it was rapidly replaced by boredom. The bustling kibbutz, booming Tel Aviv, and ancient Jerusalem had been replaced by corn fields. The cultural stimulation that he had taken for granted in his various journeys around the globe now seemed to have disappeared in a pile of smoke. Undoubtedly, he had no language difficulties now; day-to-day life was easier, and there would not be the profiling that took place in Kyoto or the frequent staring that he had borne witness to throughout Japan. He could order apple juice in a restaurant here for dinner without French looks of horror.

Nor did his behavior here represent a model of America. Here he was merely an individual, not a foreigner acting as a tourist diplomat for his country. He was without doubt an outlier here in rural Indiana, but he was an intra-national outlier, not an international one. Outliers that crossed national lines were a different breed. These outliers became entangled in linguistic, racial, and cultural barriers much more, rather than mere personality ones. However, despite this fact, he felt a greater distance from the majority of the townspeople than most of the travelers whom he had met on his journey. He had shared with these travelers a thirst for knowledge and discovery that was simply not present here. Like him, the other travelers were risk takers who were willing to leave the familiar confines of home for the uncertain waters of foreign travel. Their willingness to embrace discomfort caused their sense of awareness and perception to become much more akin to rubber bands: much more flexible and open to change. World travelers were a distinct subspecies of humans; Thomas fervently believed this in his heart and he believed that he would carry this conviction to his grave. Could anyone convince him to abandon this belief? The chances of this happening were slim to none.

He did not know yet where his next foreign entanglement would be; but it was a question of when, not if. France, Japan, and Israel had forever changed him, but this chemical formula was not yet complete. Sooner rather than later, another country would throw its elements into the mix, producing an amended Thomas Gephardt, yet again. How could he stop exploring foreign cultures after a mere three adventures? No, this plunge had simply been analogous to walking along the sand on the beach near the water. It was a promising beginning, but there were numerous uncharted waters that still lay on the horizon. He was a world adventurer, and resting on his laurels was not part of his DNA. He had a burning curiosity about a myriad number of languages and cultures. He had barely explored the Spanish-speaking world, the Slavic world, Africa, and India, just to name a few. By one means or another, Thomas would add these colors to his travel rainbow. His intellectual satisfaction and sense of purpose depended upon it.

If you would be willing to leave a review on Goodreads and any other website of your choice, it would be highly appreciated. Reviews are very helpful to authors with small publishers.

Made in the USA
Lexington, KY
24 October 2019